Hooker to Looker; a makeup guide for the not so easily offended is published under Mission books, sectionalized division under Di Angelo Publications INC.

MISSION BOOKS - an imprint of Di Angelo Publications
Hooker to Looker; a makeup guide for the not so easily offended.
Copyright 2016 Jentry Kelley in digital and print distribution in the United States of America.

For information:

Di Angelo Publications,
4265 San Felipe #1100 Houston, Texas, 77027
www.diangelopublications.com

**Library of congress cataloging-in-publications data**

Jentry Kelley
Hooker to Looker; a makeup guide for the not so easily offended
is available through digital distribution and e-book.
Downloadable via Kindle, iBooks and nook.

Registered with the Library of Congress

**Hardback:**
ISBN-10:
1942549113
ISBN-13:
978-1-942549-11-6

**E-Book:**
ISBN-10:
1942549156
ISBN-13:
978-1-942549-20-8

Layout: Chris Perez
Cover Design: Lisa Gener

1. Cosmetics
2. Non Fiction —— Fashion & Costume —— General & Miscellaneous
United States of America with international Distribution.

# "Let Me Introduce Myself"

As I always say before explaining my concepts of makeup, "Makeup is an opinion, and everybody has a different one." It's okay if you don't agree with every technique I go over in this book. Mostly, I try to teach makeup with the techniques I use to paint a face on a canvas. I stick to the basic laws of color, using light versus dark, to enhance or draw features back in. If I wouldn't do it on a canvas, I don't do it with makeup application. I also feel that you shouldn't use makeup to create something completely opposite of what you are, making yourself look like a 3rd grade art project gone bad after a box of crayons blew up in your face. I'm just here to try and keep you looking less like a Hooker, and more like a Looker.

I firmly believe makeup should only be an enhancement of who you are. I have been painting faces for over 20 years now and still work by trial and error each day. I am sure that what I am writing in this book today won't be exactly what I teach women 10 years from now. Each day I find new and better ways of doing things, because I am still evolving as an artist myself. Once an artist thinks they know everything, they become unwilling to try new techniques and they get stuck. My biggest fear in life is the feeling of being stagnant.

I am here to hold your hand and coach you to become your own artist as you apply your makeup each morning. I'll be guiding you and explaining what I have learned throughout the years as I have applied makeup to over 10,000 faces. I'm not here to candy coat anything or let you down easy. I am here to tell you what your friends won't, as you look in the mirror and say, "Is she talking about me? I do that with my makeup. Why hasn't anyone told me?" Listen, I'll tell you what your friends won't, because they are too scared to hurt your feelings. I'm not worried about your feelings; it's my job to be honest. You can resist and fight me on some of these techniques. That's fine, because I know that soon you will come around. Everyone does! Well, almost everyone. Take what you will from this book, and hopefully you will apply some of these techniques to your own daily routine. I hope what you learn makes you look and feel even more beautiful than you already are. Sit back and watch as others notice as well.

My favorite kind of feedback that I get just about every day is that others start to notice and compliment the changes in your application. My clients often tell me how they had never been complimented on their makeup in their life until I showed them the light. Many come to me saying they get stopped on a regular basis by others inquiring about the brand of makeup they are wearing. It feels really good that not only is someone noticing your beautiful flawless application, but they are even stopping to tell you how pretty you are! Every woman loves to have their beauty recognized.

After reading this book, it may come as a total shock to realize you had been doing 90% of your makeup wrong. I hear that on the regular! If it seems overwhelming, try applying the techniques one chapter at a time. In a few months, you may adopt an entirely new technique of makeup application. Who knows, I may even help you look 5-10 years younger. Who doesn't love that? In this book, I will challenge you to try something new. Step out of your comfort zone and create a brighter, more youthful version of you!

# HOOKER TO LOOKER

a makeup guide for the not so easily offended

## BY JENTRY KELLEY

# Table of Contents

# Chapter 1

## "How it All Began"

It all started with a paintbrush, during private art lessons after school in 3rd grade. Years later, I was still painting on a canvas while taking every type of art class offered as my electives in school. At the age of 14, my mom enrolled me in modeling school. Every Saturday for 13 weeks we drove into Houston in complete silence. I HATED her for making me go. I was a tomboy who hated all things girlie. I really didn't feel like I, of all people, belonged in modeling school. I was rail thin, super awkward, and had zero confidence. I still believe she sent me there just to learn how to act more ladylike and hoping that I might one day realize that other girls don't have farting contests or shop exclusively in the boy's section of a department store. I was her only child, and I was her only hope for a girl.

On the last Saturday of the 13 week modeling course, we had our makeup how-to. The makeup artist teaching the class was named Charles, and he was incredible. His basic instruction was just to get us ready for auditions: simple and clean makeup. The agency didn't want us to show up to a potential modeling job looking like a two-cent hooker, giving the agency a bad name. I remember sitting in a small 10 x 10 room with 8+ other tweens, gazing into the Hollywood lit mirrors. With my Clinique compact of City Base that was 19 shades too light in hand, I began to paint my face with that little sponge thinking, "Wow, this is just like painting a face on a canvas... but instead I am painting a face over my face! What a noble idea!" I could paint over all my insecurities, and rosacea, to create something else to feel more confident about myself. For the first time, I could actually FEEL pretty. Little did I know that four short years later I would be in one of those goofy looking white lab coats at a Clinique counter teaching other gals what I learned from Charles. Now I was able to give other girls the same level of confidence I felt that day.

11

When I enrolled in college at 18 my mom asked, "Would you like me to talk to my friend Peggy? She runs the Clinique counter over at Dillard's Baybrook. They pay $10 an hour!" Minimum wage was barely $5 back then, so I thought I was big time. It didn't take long before I was the go-to makeup girl for lessons. I can honestly say I jacked up a lot of faces before I really learned what I was doing. My motto was then, and still is today, "Fake it till you make it". This is exactly what I have been doing ever since.

After nearly 3 years at Clinique, I decided to take a job outside of makeup sales. A freelancer mentioned to me that the company she worked for by day was hiring and needed a sales rep. I was tired of listening to the older ladies over at Estee Lauder whine and complain about spider veins and back pains. I knew I wasn't going to stick around there as long as they did and die in that white lab coat behind that counter.

Shortly after, I took the job in outside sales in a completely different industry, and worked as a freelance artist for MAC on nights and weekends. The janitorial service industry wasn't the most glamorous job I had ever had, but it more than just paid the bills. I was banking for a 21 year old. It was flexible with my college schedule and I made amazing commissions when I landed a new account. But it was not for me, and I hated it. This was when I realized that money isn't everything. I knew that if I stayed I would start making too much and never be able to leave. I really missed doing makeup full time. It was what my heart needed, and my true passion.

Two years later, I attended a friend's wedding and met a manager in cosmetics at Neiman Marcus. She asked me to come apply, as they were hiring a new artist for a line called Bobbi Brown. I didn't even know who that was, but when I heard Neimans paid for part of my college tuition, I asked, "Where do I sign up?"

They assigned me to the Bobbi Brown counter and basically threw me in with trial by fire. We were busy as hell my first day and I had no clue what I was doing. Coming from MAC, known for probably the heaviest style of makeup in the industry, to Bobbi Brown, the most simple and natural makeup concept, was a huge adjustment, to say the least. I'll never forget that first poor, poor soul I helped. Well, I don't think you would call it "helped". It was more like "ruined". It took a whole lot of coaching before I really started to get it.

I was a fiery know-it-all in my younger years, with the worst case of white face makeup on the planet. The trainer for Bobbi Brown, Dottie, gave me a crash course in makeup application when she told me to remove my jacket to take a look at the color of my face versus the color of my arms and chest. The color of my face was as lily white as a porcelain doll, but my body was the color of a Brazilian beach babe. I had always wondered why I had a super white face in photos. Oh my, was she right! I was matching my face and not even looking at my body.

This was the moment when I started to realize I knew absolutely nothing about makeup. I set my pride aside and started to absorb all the new techniques I was learning. At first I didn't always agree, and some techniques I still don't use, but 90% of what I took away from their education I still teach others today. As a growing artist,

13

makeup is still just trial and error for me. It's trying something over and over again on different skin tones, age groups, and features to find what works and what doesn't while gaining more and more experience with every face you paint. Ultimately, that's how I developed my concepts. Painting a face with a makeup brush is just like painting on a canvas with acrylic. The rules of highlighting and shadowing to create dimension remain the same. I just make it all make sense for the average person without any artistic background, as they apply their makeup daily.

After five years at Bobbi Brown, I had graduated with a Bachelor's Degree in Business Management by taking night classes. I was 27 at the time, and was waiting around for the promotion to the next level, which was Counter Manager. My ultimate goal was to be an Account Executive and manage all the Bobbi Brown counters in town. When the position came open, I told my boss I wanted the job. I thought for sure I had it. I mean, I was one of the top producers at the counter and really gave 110% every day at work. I cared about my clients and loved my job. Why wouldn't they pick me? A few weeks later, our team was called into the office for an announcement. Another counter manager from another line was being promoted to the spot I had been so patiently waiting for. Soon after, one of my clients asked me if I wanted to work for her husband in his plastic surgery office. *Well, duh! Where do I sign up?* He hired me on the spot and I turned in my two week's notice at Neimans. If I wasn't going to move up there, it was time to go. When I told them I was leaving, they offered me the Laura Mercier counter manager position. I loved Bobbi so much and never understood why I wasn't worthy of that position. I felt as if I was being traded off to a lower volume counter. I was just ready for something new at that point. I turned it down and left Neiman Marcus.

Five short weeks later, the plastic surgeon fired me. He was frustrated that I couldn't assist him correctly during surgeries, and didn't like the attitude I gave him when he talked down to me. I had never been without a job before, and out of desperation called my old manager at Neimans. With my tail between my legs, I asked if the Laura Mercier counter manager position was still open. What were the chances? It was still available! This was on a Friday and I was told I would interview on Monday and start on Tuesday. Boom! I had a job again. Not exactly what I wanted, but it would do for now until I could figure out a game plan. I started back with a bad attitude and laid low for the first couple of months. I was learning the personalities of my new team while formulating my plan to prove to Bobbi Brown that they had made a mistake by not promoting me.

It was my first Beauty Week (gift with purchase) since I had become manager at Laura Mercier. We had done pretty well on our pre-sales, but Laura was never in a close running with the high volume that Bobbi brought in during these events. That morning, I showed up early to make sure all pre-sales were rung up before the store opened. As I passed the Bobbi counter, the Account Executive said to me, "We are going to beat you today," with a smirk on her face. Well, that was an obvious one. They always did! When someone tells me I can't do something, I'm only motivated to try even harder! I came back to my counter, called for a team meeting, and told my girls what the Bobbi team thought of us. That's ok, I thought, we were going to prove them wrong. They were all laughing, thinking there was no way we could pass them up. I didn't care what had to be done, we were going to beat them; and by golly we did! For the first time, we slayed the beast! Nobody believed it, and even I didn't know how it was happening. We simply focused on each of our clients individually to give them the best customer service possible. This increased our clients' trust in our process, and as a result, increased our sales. We cared about making each client feel beautiful. Through our instruction, we empowered each client to be able to do their own makeup every day with the knowledge they took home from us. More than two years later, I was still doing the same thing..... whoopin Bobbi Brown's fanny. After I took that position, we brought the counter up 30% and passed Bobbi in annual sales for the first time in history.

This experience taught me how to manage my team to work both for and with me. I learned how to order inventory in a timely manner to keep stock levels balanced, and how to build a clientele that kept coming back. By January 2011, I knew my days of working behind the makeup counter were over. I put in my notice and launched my website for my wedding makeup business. On the first day, I posted all over social media that I was finally on my own, and somehow booked over $3000 in business. About 3 months later, someone I knew suggested that I start my own line of makeup. People didn't care what brand I sold them, they just wanted something that worked. At that very moment I Googled the one company I knew manufactured makeup. A woman answered the phone and I asked the same question I am sure she gets 89 times a day, "I want to start a makeup line, what do I need to do?" She quickly replied, "We have an open house in SOHO NYC next week, you should come." So I did. I basically emptied my bank account to pay for a last minute flight and hotel to get to this open house. I spent 8-9 hours bugging the crap out of the sales reps, trying to pick colors, sort through packaging options, ask for referrals for label makers and box manufacturers, and gather any info I could. I had my pen and pad ready! At the end of the open house I said, "Okay, let's do this. I don't have any money, so how can I pay for this?" They replied, "Well, we take credit cards." Then it was done. I handed them my AMEX and there went my first transaction for $4000.

I went to college to learn how to write an incredibly detailed business plan. But I gave up on that by the second page and said to myself, "Self, we are just going to wing it. No matter what, we have to make this work." Five months later I was on the verge of an anxiety attack when I saw my AMEX balance. It was maxed out to it's $35,000 limit. In a panic, I started posting all over Facebook that I was having a two day launch party with free makeovers to get people to try the makeup line. I didn't even sell eyeshadows or mascara yet! I was just going to literally wing it. Which is exactly what I did. Nearly 200 people showed up, and we sold $10,000 in makeup.

Thank goodness, because the minimum payment on my AMEX was more than the monthly rent on my apartment. At this point all I had was my website; I wasn't in a physical location yet. People would ask where they could try the line, and the option was $200 for a private in home lesson, or free for a group makeup lesson for 6+ people in your private home. I should just sell this whole thing today and start a marketing firm, because that right there, my friends, was genius. By accident, I created this multiplier effect. For each party I did, I would book two more. Instead of meeting just one person for the lesson, I would be introduced to 5-9 of her friends. They all wanted free makeup lessons. Who doesn't want to look pretty for free!? I couldn't even make the makeup as fast as I was selling it. I had waiting lists for months. After about four months in business, while selling this makeup out of the trunk of my car, I had sold $35,000. I had earned back my entire original investment. I made $2000/mo payments towards the AMEX bill and spent every remaining dollar on more inventory. Eight months later I was referred by a fellow artist, Anthony, to my first retail store at CAMEO, office of Plastic Surgeon Dr. Forrest Roth in West Ave Shopping Center. This little Texas girl was on Cloud 9. This place was the best of the best. I could only dream of an office space like this, and he wanted to sell little ole JKC? I'll take it!

Just months later, we opened in three more stores and word spread like wildfire, most notably in Louisiana. A very close friend of mine named Sunni had introduced me to the owner of Vanessa V Boutique in Lafayette, where I began doing one on one makeup wardrobing with her cleints. Friends started telling friends that JKC was the best think since sliced bread, and in less than two years we had three stores in that state alone. By the end of 2015, exclusively by word of mouth, JKC was sold in 14 stores in 3 states. This officially made it a national brand! More than 4 years have gone by since the launch of the brand and it has grown into way more than I had ever imagined. I just believed in myself and knew I could make anything possible, if I only worked hard at it. Thus far it has worked!

The primary objective of my brand is to educate. We really want all women to look and feel as if they have their own makeup artist on staff. Most women don't have the natural gift of makeup artistry, and they fake it till they make it on the daily. We assist them, with a lot of hand holding, to actually make it! All of the tools we give to our clients (makeup homework sheets, YouTube videos, and face-to-face tutorials) are all created to help educate. This book is yet another tool to help spread the word that "less is more" when it comes to makeup. While showing women how to apply with routines that are realistic, our brushes are labeled for the products they apply, a color by number makeup homework sheet is given after each makeover, and a book like this to instruct our clients over and over until they get it. After you have mastered it, you will want to show your friends. Nobody wants friends with bad makeup, right?!

I like to use makeup as a confidence booster. While in school, I wore makeup every day, no matter how early my class was. I've always believed that when you look good, you feel good, and when you feel good, you do good! I've never regretted taking a few extra minutes in the morning to do something that made me feel better about myself. Whether you work long hours or rise before the sun, it's worth taking the extra 5 minutes in the morning to increase your confidence throughout the day!

---

# Chapter 2
## "Know and Love Your Skin"

Prepping with Skincare

Skincare can be simple. It is even simpler when made of clean ingredients and accompanied by an easy to understand order of application. Since puberty, I have personally dealt with Rosacea and Keratosis Pilaris. The symptoms look similar to a rash on the face and arms with bumps that look like white heads. If I even look at fragrance or jewelry containing nickel, I get an itchy rash like poison ivy. When I started my skincare line, I wanted to choose a formula that was: clean, fragrance free, plant based, made with organic oils, and without any irritating ingredients. Even though I do like to use glycolic acids and retinol creams, I don't like to use them daily, and neither does my skin.

Now, back to the basics. These days, many people are looking for natural, plant based products without harsh chemicals. To be honest, I always thought that organic and all natural products would be less effective, or that I wouldn't see the same results as products that claim to have more active ingredients. Recently, however, my whole idea about that has changed. I found a company at a Las Vegas cosmetics trade show that agreed with my concept and said they could make it happen. We sourced the organic oils and started the formulation process. We added ingredients that made sense. We used cucumber as the anti-inflammatory ingredient, aloe to calm and heal, hyaluronic acid to plump the skin, and arnica to lighten bruises and dark circles. All the natural way. We formulated systems that worked, without being aggressive, so they could be used daily by women with even the most sensitive skin.

I also recommend using them in conjunction with any cell turnover creams you may use at night that make your skin hypersensitive. I believe it is good to use a retinol cream in the evening, then use the aloe based products in the morning to calm redness, soothe, and heal. They work as a team to achieve the best results. You can spend all your money and time on lotions and potions, but you will see a faster result using a retinol cream at night without breaking your bank.

When you are mixing different brands, it is important that you apply all of your skincare in the correct order so they work to their full potential. The rule of thumb is always apply in order of thickness. Watery solutions first and then working towards the thicker products. I recommend exfoliating in the morning to buff all dead skin out of the way so everything penetrates deeper. Then follow with your toners, which are more like water in texture. Serums are normally lighter in texture than creams, and they go after your toners so they can slide into the skin deeper. The last product should be your thickest product, and that is your moisturizer. They are creamy in texture, and work best when applied after toners and serums.

This is the basic skincare routine that I suggest for every woman to use on a daily basis in the morning and before bed each night.

AM Routine:

1. EXFOLIATE
2. TONE
3. SERUM
4. MOISTURIZER
5. SPF


PM Routine:

1. REMOVE EYE MAKEUP
2. REMOVE FACE MAKEUP
3. TONE
4. SERUM
5. MOISTURIZER
6. RETINOL

Dermatolgist Marjory Nigro says, "New research shows that you are able to use moisturizers over and under tretinoin and retinol creams. These anti-aging creams come from a family called retinoids, which are forms of vitamin A. They work by penetrating your skin and connecting receptors like Legos. This stimulates the production of new collagen and the preservation of elastin fibers, and goes against the aging of skin." When you think VITAMIN A, think anti-aging.

Let's now analyze the natural ingredients we use on our skin and how they are useful in achieving a flawless complexion while healing acne prone skin. Below you will find a glossary of ingredients and how they affect our skin when used topically.

GLOSSARY OF INGREDIENTS

Aloe Vera- Calms, heals, and soothes the skin. Eases eczema and psoriasis flare-ups. Antibacterial. Anti-inflammatory.

Apricot oil- Light and gentle moisturizer. Does not leave a greasy coating after use. Good for sensitive skin, and especially for oily skin.

Arnica- Belongs to the sunflower family and is used mostly for medicinal purposes. Accelerates the healing process by stimulating the formation of granular tissues. Helps to lighten bruises, dark circles, and heals skin after over exposure to the sun. Anti-inflammatory, antiseptic, and antibacterial.

Avocado Oil- Contains an assortment of vitamins and minerals beneficial for the skin, and helps skin retain water. Enhances the skin's ability to generate collagen, keeping it firm while also soothing dry, itchy skin.

Beet Root Extract- Helps maintain elasticity in the skin. Feeds the skin iron and other vitamins, leading to a clearer complexion.

Castor Oil- Moisturizing and calming oil pressed from the castor bean plant. Used for centuries for natural remedies. Also strengthens and hydrates eyebrows and eyelashes.

Clover Flower Extract- used to treat specific skin conditions like eczema, psoriasis, and skin rashes. Anti-inflammatory.

Cornstarch- Anti-inflammatory that is great for itches, burns, and rashes. Used as an oil absorbent in cosmetics alongside talc.

Chamomile- Strong anti-inflammatory. Great for sensitive and acne prone skin. It calms, soothes, and is great for use after peels to promote healing the skin. Antioxidant rich.

Cucumbers- Lightens dark circles and gives instant benefits when used under the eyes. Cucumbers decrease water retention and reduces puffiness due to the large amounts of ascorbic acids they contain. Contain vitamins C and K, which are great antioxidants.

Eucalyptus Leaf- The scent of eucalyptus is meant to clear the head and cool the mind with its camphor-like aroma and woody undertone. Used for its antibacterial effects and for aromatherapy.

Grapefruit- Rich in vitamin C and a great antioxidant.

Grape Seed extract- Helps to treat acne and is a great source of antioxidants. Tightens the skin and closes up pores to avoid clogging. Anti-aging and improves elasticity. Decreases itching on dry skin.

Hyaluronic Acid- Helps skin retain moisture in the epidermis (the thin top most layer of skin). "Supercharger" for moisturizers, giving the skin an instant plumping result minimizing fine lines and wrinkles. Gives the skin a hydrated glow resulting in more youthful looking skin. It holds 2000 times its weight in water.

Japanese Green Tea- Contains caffeine which helps to shrink blood vessels to reduce dark circles.

Jojoba Oil- This oil is unique for being shockingly similar to the natural oil produced by our skin. It is readily absorbed and great to balance the skin by acting as your own oil. Made from a desert shrub.

Lavender Flower Water- Tones the skin and controls breakouts. By-product of the distillation process to make lavender oil.

Lavender Oil- Most popular oil used due to its therapeutic scent. It's an antiseptic, relieves muscle spasms, and helps with circulation. Also great to prevent and heal acne.

Lemon extract- Stimulates, clears, and tightens the skin. Great antiseptic to clear acne prone skin.

Mango Butter- Contains vitamins A, C, and E. Moisturizes and protects from sunburns and helps to heal them.

Olive oil- Provides an ideal emollient base for skincare. Light scent and rich with antioxidants and vitamin E.

Orange Peel- Rich in vitamin C, potassium, magnesium, and Calcium. Helps to renew the skin by adding clarity and radiance.

Peppermint oil- Invigorates and awakens the skin. Cool fresh scent.

Shea Butter- Full of vitamin A and extremely moisturizing. Improves eczema, dermatitis, and soothes thirsty skin.

Spearmint- Relaxes and calms, unlike peppermint. Strong minty scent with a fruity undertone. Used to soothe headaches and mental fatigue.

Soybean- Evens out pigment and discoloration in the skin. Also naturally rich in vitamin E.

White Willow Bark- Very calming and soothing for the skin. Discourages the development of acne. Many topical rosacea creams contain this ingredient because it soothes the burn.

Below is a list of all skincare products JKC has to offer, the main ingredients in each of them, and what type of skin they are for.

## Exfoliation:

EXFOLIATE- Spearmint, lemon, aloe, and apricot oil
For all skin types
Purpose: Removal of dead skin cells

The coveted dewy glow is the easiest and best way to achieve a smooth and even texture to your skin. It's the one step that I feel women do not do enough. You buy it once, put it under your counter, and forget it's there. Now it's time to go find your exfoliator and start using it.

There are many ways to exfoliate either manually or chemically. Manual exfoliation sweeps away dead skin by using products such as jojoba esters (or beads), polyurethane beads (microbeads), sand, ground nut shells, etc. in cream solutions or washes.

\*\*\* Dec 2015, President Obama bans the use of microbeads in cosmetics. The plastic beads are too small to be filtered by water treatment plants and end up in our waterways and are eaten by marine life. As of July 2017 they can no longer be manufactured here in the US, and by 2018 they can no longer be sold. Jentry Kelley Cosmetics does not use microbeads. Instead, our exfoliate contains jojoba esters which are 100% natural and biodegradable.

I believe daily exfoliation should be like brushing your teeth, and done on a consistent basis to prevent dead skin build up. It is most important to do this step in the morning versus at night because your skin cells are renewing as you sleep. I prefer one clean polish before applying makeup because it looks more natural when applied to a smooth surface. Take about a dime-sized amount of the exfoliator, and lightly buff in a circular motion on the skin. Start with the place where you feel it is most rough, and dead skin tends to collect. Polish for about 10 seconds and then move to the next spot. Once all areas are exfoliated, rinse with water. The aloe vera in this product will help calm and heal the skin from exfoliation. The lemon is a natural antiseptic that will help kill any bacteria that can cause acne. It also contains apricot oil, so your skin isn't left feeling tight and dry.

If you use a chemical exfoliator at night, such as retinol or glycolic acids, they will loosen up skin cells while you are sleeping. In the morning, you can gently buff them off. Every person's skin can tolerate a different level of exfoliation, so listen to your skin and stop if it feels like it's irritated. I like to use the analogy of sand paper. At the hardware store you will find anything from a light grit sand paper to a coarse grit. You will notice that the coarse grit paper has larger particles that remove more wood quickly in the sanding process. If you have sensitive skin, of course, the harsher exfoliator would cause major irritation and feel uncomfortable if too abrasive. We want smooth, even texture without causing irritation or a raw burning sensation. My brand of exfoliator is recommended to be used as a daily scrub since it is a light to medium texture. Most people can use it daily as a cleanser and buffer. However, those with highly delicate skin should try using it only once a week until they reach the level of exfoliation they feel comfortable with. By using a light to medium grit exfoliator daily, you keep the dead skin cell build up to a minimum. Skin with rough, dry, dead skin cell build up looks aged and weathered. Lines, wrinkles, and pores also appear deeper and the skin can look dull. Your pores can also get clogged with blackheads from dirt, oil and makeup getting trapped inside. But not all exfoliators are created equal. Some made of ground nuts are really abrasive and can only be used once a week. Read the instructions on the bottle and follow the recommended frequency of use.

Chemical exfoliators encourage the skin to turn over at a deeper level, causing it to start to peel and fall off. They work by dissolving the "glue" that holds the skin cells together, allowing them to fall off so newer brighter skin cells can show. This is a great way to speed up the process of exfoliation, and in my opinion, the cheapest way to achieve the best results for anti-aging.

## Toner:

QUENCH- Cucumber, lavender flower water, cornstarch, beet root, and aloe
For all skin types
Purpose: Plump up skin cells

This step is sooooo important! It's also the one I notice most women skip without thinking twice. Mostly because they don't understand the importance, or they are using the wrong formula. Forget what you were told in the 1980's and 1990's about toners/astringents. Modern toners are like your eight glasses of water and send a surge of hydration to your skin cells, plumping them full of water like a grape. Using toners that contain alcohol do the opposite and shrivel the skin cells turning them from a grape to a raisin. You don't want to look like a dried up prune, do you? Your doctor may suggest using products like this for drying out acne. But if this is not the case, you should not be using drying products on your skin. Verify the ingredients on what you are using and look for formulas that contain items such as cucumber, aloe, and chamomile.

My formula is a thick hydrating water that locks in hydration by plumping up the skin cells. When they are healthy and full of water, they absorb more of the ingredients in your serums and creams. The formula contains lavender flower water and cucumber to hydrate and to reduce inflammation. I never recommend using a cotton ball or pad to apply toners. Use a toner with a mister or pour into the palms of your hands and press into the skin. Cotton absorbs the product, leading to excessive use of toner which makes you run out in half the time. With my packaging, it's measured out to be one pump per use for all products. It may not feel like it's enough, which means you were previously using too much.

## Serum:

REVIVE- Arnica, aloe, and cucumber
For all skin types
Purpose: Reduces redness in the face, minimizes dark circles or bruising, and reduces puffiness in the eye area. Helps to heal after deep skin treatments or sunburns

Serums are like taking vitamins for the skin. They focus on meeting specific needs, but are not mandatory to use. If you go to the vitamin store and say that you're looking for something for your immune system, they will sell you vitamin C. If you say your nails are thinning and your hair is falling out, they will sell you biotin. If you do not have any specific skin issues, go ahead and skip this step completely. If you look in the mirror and all you see is discoloration and sun damage, then try using a serum that focuses on breaking melanin apart and lightening it. Look for items with hydroquinone or those that contain vitamin C. The one I make is great for people who have rosacea, puffy eyes due to inflammation, and dark circles. If the dark circles are the color of your skin, this one will not lighten pigment. Arnica is the ingredient that lightens bruises. If your dark circles are from pressure around the eye and nose area, caused by surgery or allergies, this serum is ideal. Arnica is said to increase the number of white blood cells sent to the area to assist in the "clean up" helping the bruise fade quicker. The cucumber in this product is a great anti-inflammatory for puffy eyes.

## Moisturizer:

BALANCE- Jojoba oil, avocado, grape seed, soybean, and hyaluronic acid
For heavy T-zones, or oily skin types
Purpose: To balance oil levels in the skin. Tricks your skin to feel hydrated so you don't produce as much oil

HYDRATE- Mango butter, avocado oil, lavender oil, cucumber, grape seed, and hyaluronic acid
For combination to dry skin types
Purpose: To feed the dry areas without over hydrating the oily areas

ENRICH- Shea butter, grape seed extract, lavender oil, olive, grapefruit, jojoba, soybean and hyaluronic acid.
Dry skin types, all skin types in PM
Purpose: Rich moisturizer to comfort and soothe dry skin. Works to help heal specific dry skin conditions naturally. Balances the hydration levels of all skin types while sleeping. Excellent night cream.

We will start by addressing oily skin. I know it's really hard to believe that you need to add oil to your oil slick, but it's true. If your skin is being fed products that contain alcohol that dry it out, your overactive oil glands go into heavy production and start cranking out even more. Your skin will try to make more of what you just stripped it of, trying to balance it out. But if you give it a little bit of oil, something like a jojoba that's very close to the natural oil on your skin, the skin will feel quenched without the need to produce more to compensate. My BALANCE formula is the best option for this skin type.

We also carry an amazing product to help control oil from coming to the surface in those problem areas. Shine Down Mattifying Gel is a silicone based polymer that fills in the pores, keeping you drier longer. It also contains a small amount of witch hazel to keep the skin drier. Many other cosmetic companies sell similar products and are great to use after your skincare and before you apply makeup. Try applying the product only in the areas that produce heavy oil, and not all over. Don't let me forget to mention they will also be great to fill in fines lines and wrinkles. Nobody wants to see those!

The combination skin type is the most common. When I ask a client what type of skin they have, and they don't really know the answer, they are combination. You will know if you're oily, and you will know if you're extremely dry. But a combination skin is when you have areas with both. Normally the oil will be in the center of your face, forehead, and chin areas. You may notice that your cheeks and the outer edges of your face feel dryer. This is the skin type that uses HYDRATE cream. It contains mango butter, avocado oil, and lavender oil which help to balance the skin out. It hydrates where it feels dry without making the oily places feel too greasy.

I want to address how important it is to drink a ton of water to hydrate from the inside out. You can use fantastic creams on the surface, but if you're not hydrated internally it's going to show in your skin. As we get older, our skin tends to get drier as time goes on. If you were oily in your teenage years, you may become combination in your 30's and dry in your 50's. Typically after menopause, your skin will become drier as your oil production slows. This is when it's extremely important to add extra hydration and boost up your moisturizer. If you are postmenopausal, you are most likely to have dry skin, and you will use my ENRICH formula of moisturizer. The first ingredient is shea butter, which is extremely moisturizing. If you feel most creams that you apply in the morning make you feel dry again by lunchtime, this moisturizer is for you. It makes your skin feel quenched all day. It's also great to use to soothe dry skin conditions like eczema and psoriasis. You don't have to be completely bone dry to use this product. We actually recommend use of this on all skin types in the evening. When you are sleeping, your skin cells are renewing themselves and it's most important to boost your hydration during this time. Even oily skin needs to boost hydration in the evening. I have combination to dry skin, and always look forward to putting on the ENRICH cream after I wash my face before I go to bed.

## SPF - Sun Protection Factor

When to apply: Sunscreen should be applied to the top most layer of your skin daily
For all skin types
Purpose: To reflect light, and prevent UVA and UVB rays from being absorbed into your skin

Sunscreen works best when applied to the top layer of your skin. It should either be applied after your skincare, or formulated inside of your foundation or primer. You will reflect more sun if it's not covered up by five layers of creams, primer, and foundation. Average daily recommended sunscreen is between SPF 15-30. If you are outside for an extended period of time, you should always apply a higher level of sunscreen under your makeup. My primer has SPF 20 and my foundation has an SPF 15. That way, if you wear one without the other you still have protection. Also note that if you use more than one product with SPF, you do not add the two SPFs together to determine the amount of sun protection. Used together, SPF 15 and SPF 20 do not equal SPF 35, silly. You will just have SPF 20.

## Removers:

ERASE- Castor oil, cucumber, and aloe
All skin types. Not recommended for eyelash extensions
Purpose: Removes eye makeup gently, and conditions the eyelashes

Taking off makeup before going to bed is one of my favorite subjects. I'm not gonna sit here and say that I always practice what I preach, but I'm still going to preach to you the right way to do it anyway. Right after that I am going to go over the wrong way as well.

During the day when you're walking through a shopping mall, or getting on the elevator and pressing the button to your floor, you were touching all sorts of nasties. Boogers, bacteria, and human feces are found on nearly every handrail, doorknob, and elevator. Then you reach up and scratch your face, or touch your eye. If I'm being completely honest here, you bring all of that home with you, and you want to lie on your pillow without taking off your makeup at night? It's gross. Listen, I am the first to say that I'm not perfect. It's hard to believe, I know, but many nights I crawl into bed with all of my makeup on. Sometimes I am just too physically exhausted to get up to go wash my face the right way. But that's what makeup face wipes are for, right? Can I get an AMEN? They sit on my nightstand and at least I can get the majority of the junk off my face. Another analogy here: It's like taking a sponge bath versus getting in the shower and rinsing everything off your body with bar soap. It's still better than sleeping in it and transferring all of that onto your pillow case to put your face on next night.

I recommend first removing the eye makeup with a cotton pad, then your face makeup. This way any residue that you pushed over to the side of your face can be rinsed off when you take off your foundation. My new formula of eye makeup remover with castor oil really does help it slide off so much easier. Try not to rub or tug in the eye socket area when removing your makeup. Gently swipe back and forth until all eye makeup is removed. When you scrub around the eye area, you can break the capillaries causing more dark circles. So be as gentle as possible. The castor oil also helps condition the lash as you remove the makeup, so make sure you're also putting some on your eyebrows. People tend to neglect their lashes and brows. They need to be conditioned and hydrated just like you do your hair and skin. When they are hydrated it protects them from getting brittle, gives more shine and lengthens the lash.

UNDRESS- Eucalyptus, lavender, clover flower extract, and willow bark
All skin types
Purpose: To remove the face makeup and to cleanse the skin

Something you may not know is that not all cleansers are makeup removers. Some cleansers only remove dirt and oil, but do not break down foundation. You end up just swishing it around on the skin. When you go to dry off your face, you see makeup all over your white face towel. That's because you never really removed the makeup. It's like jumping in the shower with all of your clothes on and bathing over your clothes. You have to use something that breaks down the makeup and removes it to cleanse the skin. My remover has eucalyptus, which gives a really clean, fresh feel to the skin. It also contains willow bark, which calms and soothes the skin without irritation, and helps to prevent acne. I recommend dampening the skin and using one pump of this gel cleanser, massaging it until you get a lather. Once it turns white, then it starts to break down the makeup and removes it from your face. You will feel squeaky clean when it's all over. If you wear full coverage foundation, I suggest repeating the step twice to make sure all makeup is removed. Once the makeup is removed, you follow with the same 3 steps as you do in the A.M., skipping the exfoliate.

## Lip Hydration:

LIP DEW SPF 15

Avocado oil, aloe, and vitamin C - For dry lips
Purpose: Lip hydration without drying ingredients.

Have you ever heard someone say that they are addicted to Chap Stick? It's because they literally are. A lot of companies that sell lip balms add ingredients that dry your lips so you keep coming back for more. It's a great marketing idea, because you end up with 18 tubes. Some under the seat of your car, at your desk, your nightstand, your bathroom, next to your recliner...you get the point. You feel like if you don't have it at arm's reach to apply on your lips consistently, that they are going to crack and fall off. That's why our lip moisturizer only hydrates. Even though it looks neon orange in the tube, it goes on sheer with a silky feel, with a surge of vitamin C injected in the center. Instead, this one moisturizes all day. I recommend using this product in the morning before makeup, and at night after your skincare routine. I am a lip picker. If I don't have something on my lips at night I will pick them until they bleed. I have to put this on every night before I go to bed, and I actually get excited about doing it. Feels delicious!

## Hyaluronic acid:

I learned about this product only a few years before launching my skin care line. When I reformulated my skin care to the new organic version in 2015, I added hyaluronic acid to all of my face creams. Next to arnica, it is one of my favorite ingredients. I am a sucker for instant results, and you get instant results with this guy. Hyaluronic acid (HA) is something that our body produces naturally. It's the jelly like substance between collagen and elastin fibers. I always give the analogy that it's like the spring to your mattress. When we are younger we produce tons of it and our skin is very padded. Think of a five-year-old's squishy cheeks. As we get older the HA production slows, and we lose volume in our lips, cheeks, and temples. After menopause, your body says, "I'm retiring and I'm not making that stuff for you anymore, so good luck with that." This is when we really start to see our face aging. HA is the same ingredient found in dermal fillers that nurses like Bri Lynn Collins, RN, inject into your lips and cheeks to add more volume. By the way, she is the only hooker I let poke me in the face with needles. Topically, HA does not serve as a substitute for the same result. When it is applied to your epidermis, it holds 2000 times its weight in water and gives instant dewy and radiant glow. I don't know about you, but I like instant results. If it says it takes six weeks to see results, I'm over it. I already forgot what I looked like six weeks ago.

*Please note:*
I believe that knowing your skin type and communicating your skin issues with your skincare specialist or dermatologist is important to achieving the skin you desire. If your skin issues linger, try doing a skin allergy test to eliminate any products from your regimen that cause irritation to your skin. Playing the guessing game will prolong the issues that you're having with your skin. When the test results come back, you'll know exactly which ingredients that you're allergic to and what to avoid.

---

JENTRY KELLEY

Tinted Primer
Broad Spectrum
SPF 20

Medium

1 fl. oz. (30 mL)

# Chapter 3
## "Prep, Prime, and Spackle"

Primer, Foundation, Concealer, and Powder

Throughout my career as an artist, my style of makeup has gone from a heavy full coverage matte to more of a weightless look with a dewy glow. Makeup styles change, just like fashion does, and I think it's important to stay on trend so you stay modern. I've never heard someone say, "Date me with makeup and make me look 20 years older." Ok, maybe I heard it once, but she was a little crazy.

I remember it being a big adjustment for me to go from MAC foundation powder to a luminous look with Bobbi Brown. It felt a little sticky and oily, which I wasn't used to. When I created my line, I wanted something that didn't feel like I had anything on, and didn't look like it either. I love skin that looks naked, yet flawless, with a sheer glow. You can't achieve that look with dry matte foundation and powder. Matte foundation ages the skin and amplifies any lines, wrinkles, or textures in the skin. This isn't an opinion of mine, it's a fact. Dewy reflects light and looks hydrated, and matte dries and dulls without reflection. It was hard to make the change to a dewy look, but after I did, I saw what Bobbi Brown was always talking about. My friends started noticing and complimenting my skin. It's funny how nobody mentioned anything when I wore heavy matte foundation. As soon as I made the switch to a weightless dewy foundation, people were saying, "I'm so glad you stopped wearing all that heavy foundation. You didn't need it. Your skin doesn't look all caked up now." The thing was, I didn't have less makeup on. I just made the switch to a dewy formula. Friends should tell friends when they have bad makeup! I always do. But now that I look back, I see where they were coming from and wish I had known sooner. This is why I want to share my beauty tips with all of you: to spare you from making all the bad makeup mistakes I made myself.

## Step One: Primer

Just like priming a wall before you paint it, I also suggest doing this before applying makeup. Primers come in a variety of different formulas ranging from clear mattifying type gels that control oil, to hydrating primers that give your skin a glow, allowing your foundation to glide on smoother.

Shine Down Oil Control Gel can be used after skincare and before makeup to put the brakes on any oil that's waiting to overflow to the surface. This will prevent foundation from breaking apart in these areas. Apply only to the areas with heavy oil production. There are other brands that make similar mattifying primers as well in this clear gel formula. When using this type of product I recommend applying with the tips of the fingers and massaging into the skin until the consistency goes from a gel, to a velvet, and dries to a smooth powder consistency. No need to wait before applying foundation.

The two most common skin types are combination and dry. With these skin types I like to use the Tinted Primer SPF 20 from my line. Not only does it prep the skin for foundation, it has enough coverage to wear alone for a more casual, weightless look. As the name implies, there are three steps in one tube: primer, a touch of sheer foundation, and sunscreen. It's easy for beginners, women who naturally have flawless skin and just need to tone down redness, and for those who want to achieve a dewy glow. There are only four shades. Each color option matches three different skin tones, so you only have to be in a range of color. This means if you lightly tan, you don't have to change colors. If you go from porcelain doll to Hawaiian tropic model, you will need to bump up a shade in the summer. But for the most part, you have wiggle room for color matching.

The amount varies per person, but I always recommend starting out with less than a dime-sized amount applied to the back of your hand. You can always add more if needed. When applying any liquid or cream products to the skin, I suggest using a synthetic hair foundation brush. Brushes made of real hair don't work as well for creamy formulations, and tend to clump the brush hair together and cake up at the tip of the brush. A slick, firm bristle is the best choice in my opinion. Makeup sponges are my least favorite option because they hold bacteria and absorb too much makeup that tends to get lost during application. You could use your fingers, but after reading below you may see why I prefer a brush in my application.

Using a brush is all about the technique. It's important to work the makeup into the skin instead of just swiping across the face and calling it a day. Start the application by pressing the brush loaded with tinted primer onto the center of the face. This is the area where we need the most amount of coverage. Then swipe in an outward sweeping motion to blend and give an even veil of coverage.

*Basic Technique of Application:*

SWIPE to sheer the makeup.
TWIST to fill in pores, or any imperfections, with the tip of the brush.
TAP to add coverage with the flat side of brush, in areas where needed.

I typically do most of the twisting motion in the T-zone area where the pores tend to be larger. I also twist the brush in the area between the brows, on and around the nose, and on the chin. The oilier the skin, the larger the pores, and the more twisting you will be doing. For all skin types and pore sizes, make sure to twist in the outer creases of the nose to get the hard to reach areas with the tinted primer.

Use the tapping technique over any area that needs additional coverage. Just like painting on a canvas, this allows you to lay a fuller coverage only in those areas where needed. Keep going back to your hand that you are using as a palette and lay it on the skin until the blemish is invisible.

Always avoid putting primer or foundation in the eye socket area. This is one of the most common mistakes in makeup application. When you apply the primer or foundation to the eyelids it creases your eyeshadow fairly quickly. If you are guilty of doing this, by noon your eye makeup has most likely melted to the crease of your eye. When you apply any product to your eyelid (moisturizer, foundation, or concealer) it creates a slip and slide reaction when eyeshadows are later applied. The only product that should be applied to your eyelid is an eye base, which is mentioned later. As for the lower part of the eye, the layers of primer, foundation, and concealer will become too thick, causing the under eye to cake up and make you look 187 years old.

## Step Two: Foundation

This may be one of my most favorite steps in makeup. I have always struggled with uneven skin tone which has made me super self-conscious of my face without makeup. I'm German and Irish, genetically one of the most delicate and sensitive skin types. Personally, I've never been able to use face makeup with any type of perfume, or heavy oils. The bumps and rosacea on my face would flare up and my eyes would itch and burn. I have literally tried almost every foundation on the market, trying to find the perfect one. It was either fragrant, greasy in texture, too sheer or too matte, or worse... slid off my nose mid-day.

Was I really asking too much to have an all-day wear makeup that stayed on for 12 hours? Something that didn't break apart and slide off my nose by lunch, had great coverage but was luminous so it didn't look cakey, and without oil in it? I've always loved a good creamy compact foundation, but I was going through a compact in 30 days flat.

For my line of cosmetics, I wanted something that was whipped in texture, that looked like butter on the skin. By butter, I mean smooth, not greasy. I wanted to offer shades that had pink/red undertones AND shades with yellow/olive. Some brands focus on one or the other, but I wanted to cover the whole spectrum. We are all so different and should have a color that matches our skin without having to mix shades or adjust with powders.

Now, to my favorite part about my favorite step. Color matching! For a decade, I ruined every photo I was in with my friends due to my 'White Face Syndrome'. In the photo below, notice how chalky white my makeup was compared to the others. This wasn't an issue with the flash, it was an issue with my color selection.

I knew I was matching the skin on my face in person, and could not understand why my face looked like a chalkboard in photos. Why me? Was my makeup not photogenic? Was it the SPF? I never once thought it was because my foundation was 14 shades too light.

It wasn't until my trainer at Bobbi Brown, Dottie asked me, "What are you trying to match? Your face or your body?" I wanted to reply back to her, "What the hell do you think I'm matching? My FACE, silly! Should I be matching my big toe?" But I held back and let her finish. "Take off your suit jacket and look at your chest and arms. Now that is where you need to be looking," as she pointed to my chest. She finished with, "You should never match your makeup to your face." It was at that very moment that I realized what I was doing wrong.

As hard as it was to admit, she was right. It didn't matter what color my face was. After all, I wore SPF on my face every day, got in tanning beds like a bad girl, and always covered my face with a towel. My face without makeup was so much lighter toned than my body. She was a GENUIS. She taught us how to color match the foundation to the color of the chest, because that's what really mattered. Immediately after that class, the color of my foundation in photos was perfect. No more ghost face!

If you or a friend are a victim of ghost face makeup, keep reading. The color of the skin on your face doesn't matter. You are about to cover it with makeup! Take a cotton swab with a good amount of foundation and swipe on your upper chest with 3-4 shades of makeup you think would work. Let it dry for about a minute and then choose the color that disappears into your skin the most. Remember, when you apply the makeup that matches your chest and you stand back 4-5 feet from the mirror you will be all one color. You have to look at your skin as a whole. And never, I repeat NEVER, match the foundation to your neck or the underside of your forearm. It's not Estee Lauder circa 1993. Those areas mentioned are the lightest part of your whole body and you will be guaranteed to have paste face in no time.

As you apply the correct color foundation for the first time, you may think it is too dark as it slides across the virgin, untanned skin on your face. Just have faith in me, because I was once you. Once you have a coat of primer and foundation all across the skin you will start to flow with the rest of your body and become one. You won't be able to tell that the foundation is darker than the skin underneath it.

Foundation is to be applied with the same brush and technique as the primer. Swipe to sheer, twist to fill in, and tap to add coverage. I use the same amount of primer as I do foundation and work from the back of my hand as a palette. This helps me use only what I need. If you use the Tinted Primer, you will already have a veil of coverage across your skin. Some women then apply foundation in a tapping motion only in the areas where they need more coverage. I prefer using my foundation in a medium to full coverage coat all across my face, over the primer, avoiding the eye socket area for reasons mentioned above. In the areas where I have rosacea or sun damage, I grab more of the product from the back of my hand and keep laying it on in a tapping motion until those areas are flawless and blended.

Also, make sure you never apply foundation past the jawline and onto the neck area. The horizontal creases in our neck collect the foundation and it starts to separate and enhance the lines. Not to mention leaving makeup all over your collar. It may not be as noticeable in dim light, but when you walk into daylight the person standing next to you can see every streak of foundation on your neck. We have a solution to adjusting the white neck in the next chapter. So don't worry for now about the white neck next to the darker chest and face. As long and those two areas match, you can move to the next step.

## Step Three: Concealer

Another one of my favorite mistakes people make is applying a concealer that is too light. If you look like you have reflectors under your eyes in photos, you might be one of the gals I am speaking to right now. Concealers are meant to brighten and lift the under eye area without looking obvious. This trend of pure white concealer under the eyes is really unflattering in person and in photos. Let's get back to the basics here.

Concealer should be brighter, not whiter than the rest of your face. If you have a medium to darker skin tone, try a warmer pink or peach tone instead of a yellow. Yellow is best used to tone down red on lighter skin. But with warmer skin tones, it just looks white, and it's obvious that you are trying to cover something. Many people with dark circles think all their problems are solved when they find the lightest color concealer on the market. This is untrue. Concealers with a peach or pink tone actually correct blue, green, or dark pigment so much better. It's the law of color. If you have dark blue circles and use a light yellow concealer, it turns grey.

Try a warm concealer with a pink tone. When a woman with hereditary dark brown pigment under her eye uses a yellow concealer, it looks ashy. Instead, use a peach or deep honey tone and it will correct the brown and lift the shadow instantly.

In the world of cosmetics I have seen green correctors, color wheels with all primary and secondary colors, and pure yellow pigment. If you aren't an artist, this is confusing and hard to work with, so stay away. Keep it simple and find a shade that works alone without having to layer multiple shades. Very rarely (less than 1% of the time) do I feel the need to use a corrector and a concealer. Most of the time a concealer will work on its own if it's matched correctly.

When applying a concealer I recommend using a brush. You end up with better coverage and a more precise edge. Start towards the outer corner of the eye and apply the concealer in an upwards motion towards the end of the brow. This creates an illusion of light making it look as if you had a really tight ponytail in, or like you have had a lower eye lift. The outer corner of our eye tends to droop down, making the eye look tired. By using this technique you can turn that frown upside down!

Go back and grab more of the product and lay on the concealer around the upper nose area towards the inner part of the brow in a patting motion to add more coverage. Remember, tapping the brush adds more coverage and swiping the brush sheers it out. Also make sure you go directly underneath the lower lash line to reduce any redness. Like I always say when it comes to concealer, whenever you think you have enough, add more. When it looks like you have 14 pounds of concealer underneath your eye, it's probably the right amount. It's going to look cakey as you apply it, but it's supposed to. Once all the concealer is laid underneath the eye area, you can then tap with your finger to make it look more like skin. The warmth of your finger and your fingerprint will start to breakdown and texturize the concealer, making it look more believable. The key is to make it look like you didn't try. Keep blending the edge of your concealer into the foundation until you do not see an edge between the two. A good concealer should have an oil in it with hydrating properties. This creates more luminosity where we have the most lines and wrinkles. Matte concealers only amplify these lines. Unfortunately, this is the reason why concealers can't be used on the lid. I wish there was a one size fits all product in cosmetics that worked everywhere on the face, but there is not. As mentioned before, when these hydrating concealers end up on the eyelid, the makeup applied over it starts to slide around. Then, all of a sudden your eyeliner is in your crease.

When applying a concealer to the face to hide sun damage, redness, or blemishes, always make sure you apply it in step three. Primer and foundation must be applied first. If you apply your concealer to the face in the first step you will wipe it off when you put the primer and foundation on. It's best to conceal the under eyes and what's left on the face to cover all at the same time. Then you can set with powder.

## Step Four: Face Powder

There are three basic types of powder. Translucent powder, lightweight coverage powder, and a full coverage foundation powder. They range from talc to mineral based to heavy foundation powders.

Talc powders are great to smooth the texture of the skin and also to help absorb oil. Mattifying Oil Blot Powder is the talc based translucent setting powder that I offer. After applying your primer, foundation, or a combination of the two, just set with a translucent powder when you feel like you have the coverage you need. After you apply your primer or foundation, or both, if you feel like you have the coverage that you need, just set with a translucent powder. Anytime you apply creamy products to the skin, you must set with a powder or else it will begin to transfer and slide. This will insure your makeup stays on your face and off your cell phone and your clothing.

If you have an oily T-zone, this type of powder is the best on the market to carry with you to use as a touch-up. Instead of touching up with a heavy powder over your oil, foundation, and powder that you applied earlier in the morning, this one absorbs all the oil off the surface. It literally makes you look like you took it all off and redid your makeup. We use it for HD television or photography because it makes the skin looks so smooth without looking ultra-matte.

If you feel you need a little extra coverage, try Medium Coverage Face Powder to polish up anything that the foundation didn't cover. This is a mineral based powder that also gives the skin more of a dewy glow. With either of the powders mentioned above I recommend using a powder brush. I am also not a fan of sponges to apply powder. With powder, it isn't about the product being absorbed into the sponge. Instead, it's the oil and bacteria that you are pulling off your face and leaving to sit directly on the powder. It absorbs into the powder and you can see it when you begin to get those shiny bumps on your pressed powder and you are unable to retrieve the product. It's ruined at that point, and quite frankly it's gross. For on the go, try a kabuki brush for touch up. Kabuki means a dense brush with a short handle, small enough to zip into a cosmetic bag for travel. This way you aren't leaving the brush to sit directly on the product in your compact. The brush can be taken our of your bag and cleaned once a month to avoid the spread of bacteria on your compact powder.

My least favorite type of powder is a foundation powder. Some brands recommend using these as a substitute for liquid foundation. Most of these formulas seem to look really thick and matte on the skin, and not as natural as liquid. Back to what I was saying earlier. I like skin to look like skin, and powder is not skin-like in texture. When you use a full coverage powder, it accentuates any imperfections such as scars, wrinkles, large pores, and texture from dryness, especially if foundation powder is applied over liquid foundation. It's like you are applying your foundation twice.

When choosing a brush to apply powder, use this simple rule of thumb. The softer the hair, the softer the application. The stiffer, more densely packed the hair, the heavier the application. When placing the powder into the compact, try not to dig the power out. You will pick up too much product and deposit that on the first area the brush touches. Layer the powder lightly until you achieve the desired consistency, while retaining your healthy glow. Ultimately, you are using powder to set the makeup and keep it from transferring, not to dry out the skin completely. Also, remember to set your concealer with a light amount of powder to keep all of the products in place, and to avoid creasing under the eyes.

---

# Chapter 4
## "Get Cheeky"

Bronzer, Blush, and Highlighter

This is where we begin to talk about the evolution of makeup. It is also the step that most women tend to never update after high school. Rouge, as blush was once referred to, was created by the ancient Egyptians by crushing berries. It was applied to both men and women to give a flushed glow on the cheeks and lips. In the Middle Ages, it became increasingly popular and more socially acceptable when Queen Elizabeth would whiten her skin with paint, then apply rouge.

Oh, how makeup has changed in recent years with the introduction of bronzer. Now it isn't just being used just for stage and drag makeup. It has been adopted into the everyday routine of most women in order to shadow and enhance their features. In the late 1980's and early 1990's, the trend of blush application was to apply from the ear to the nose. I still see this today and it makes my blood boil. The most modern technique is to use bronzer in the places where most women are still applying their blush. The 1980's just called, and they want their blush back. Time for an update, ladies! I can spot you from a mile away with those racing stripes on your cheeks, and it's making me cringe.

If you haven't introduced a bronzer into your regimen, today is the day. Start by selecting a color that matches the undertone of your skin. Focus on the color of your upper chest and arms. If you tan more red, you will need the Warm Contour Bronzer. If you tan more olive, you will need the Golden Contour Bronzer. Your shade of bronzer should be an enhancement of your skin tone, only a few shades darker. I have kept it simple with just two shades, and neither have shimmer. It is beyond me why cosmetic companies would put something frosty or glittery into a product used to create shadows. Wait, I know why they do it. Things with glitter are pretty, and we are drawn to them, and want to buy them. They sell more products with shimmer! Bronzers should be matte, period. Again, I go back to the basics of painting on a canvas. I would never choose a bronze metallic paint to shadow a person's features. Shimmer reflects light and pulls things forward, and darker matte colors help to bring the features in, creating more dimension. If you own a bronzer that contains shimmer, congratulations you now have a new eyeshadow color to be used on your eyelid. Please stop applying this as bronzer. Thank you, and you're welcome.

When applying bronzer, it is important to find a brush that fits your coverage needs. I prefer a more natural look, so I choose to use a softer brush for a softer application. In my line, I have a brush called the Sheer Buffing Brush that I most commonly grab from my arsenal of brushes. I like how I can build the coverage, and go back for more if I need it. If you are looking for a heavier application, and a deeper contour, try a blunt cut brush with more densely packed hair. Mine is called the Flat Contour Brush. This will pick up more color, and lay it on thicker, offering a more dramatic look.

Now, where should we apply bronzer? If you are saying to yourself, "The artist who did my makeup last told me to apply where the sun hits my face for a glow!" You were lied to. If you apply bronzer all over, which should be a few shades darker than your skin, what is that going to look like? It's what we in the industry refer to as "Pumpkin Face." It's like wearing a face powder six shades too dark. You aren't giving yourself a glow, you are mudding up your skin. Honey, you just look plain silly. If you think you are giving yourself a tan with bronzer, you messed this part up too. Unless of course, you are dusting that powder all over your chest and arms while you are at it. If this is the case, let me introduce you to a self-tanner. This is a much better technique to be faking your tan with. Plus, you can apply all over!

## Step One: Bronzer

Before you begin to apply bronzer to the face, step back from the mirror and check out the color of your neck. In the previous chapter, we discussed not applying liquid makeup past the jawline. If you suffer from white neck, which most of us do, the only product you should put on the neck to warm it up is your bronzer. The sun casts a shadow and we don't get much of a tan on the upper neck area. I start the application of bronzer behind the ears where the sun doesn't shine, and I buff from one side of the neck to the next. Keep blending until the entire neck area is the same color as the chest. Apply on and below the jawline and blend downward towards the collarbone. The greatest part about this technique, is that it instantly takes five pounds off the neck. Remember, adding shadows to the face without shimmer brings things up and in, making them look slimmer. If your neck remains lighter than your face and chest, it looks like your neck is coming down or forward. Nobody wants that part of their body to come forward. So let's tuck that in with bronzer, and make it all match. White neck is super obvious in photographs, so thumb through some of your photos and see if you are a victim of White Neck Syndrome. This might just be your favorite trick in this whole book. I'll never forget how shocked I was when someone told me I had white neck. I guess I just never looked. Now it's all I look at when I'm talking to other people.

Once the neck matches the rest of the body, it's time to warm up and add dimension to the face. The guideline that I give for bronzer on the cheeks is from the center of the ear to the side of the nostril. Make sure you're applying the bronzer on and below the cheekbone, and not above the cheekbone. If you apply it too high, you will push the cheekbones back and flatten the face. Instead, we want to add a shadow below the cheekbone, which makes the cheekbone appear as if it's coming forward. When you shadow an object, the highlight around it should come forward giving a more three dimensional look. These are just basic laws of shadowing when painting on a canvas. Make sure you get the brush underneath your sideburns and upper ear area. Your sideburns cast a shadow on your face, and it's usually a bit lighter underneath the hair in that area. If you end up pulling your hair back, it becomes obvious that you have bronzer on. By adding a shadow in these areas, it makes it look blended and more natural. Then, I apply the bronzer into the temples to avoid making it look like a stripe across the face. Applying bronzer to the forehead is optional. If you have a smaller forehead or bangs, there is no need to apply in those areas. If you are trying to create the illusion of a smaller forehead, blend the bronzer all across the hairline to meet each temple. For average sized foreheads, I just lightly blend bronzer along the edge of the hairline. Bronzer can also be lightly applied to the chin to push it back if needed.

I will speak more to modern day "contouring" in another chapter later in this book. I've never been so over anything in my entire life. What you see on Instagram is overdone and over edited. It doesn't look like that in person. Extreme highlighting and shadowing (a.k.a. contour) has gone too far. It's obvious to other people when they see you in the daylight, and you look like a dirty mannequin. Just try using the regular ole powder bronzer mentioned above and quit watching those videos online. I'm doing you a favor here. You will still see results with the techniques I listed, but they will be so much more believable. Natural beauty is refreshing ladies. Leave the over contouring for the ladies of the night.

## Step Two: Blush

Now, onto your favorite part... the blush tutorial. Blush is supposed to make you look like you're flushing, or blushing. This happens in the center of the face, on the apples of your cheek. I'm not quite sure who came up with applying blush from the ear to the nose, but it looks very unnatural, not to mention outdated by 20-25 years. Using a pink or a coral shade of blush from the ear to the nose does not look believable. This is the area, as discussed above, where bronzer should go. Bronzer creates a more realistic look of a shadow or contour.

When applying blush, I choose a brush with a smaller head and angled bristles. Using a full head powder brush to apply blush is going to look like Bozo did your makeup, with pigment from your lash line to your chin. Using a brush with a smaller angled head gives you more precision in your application. Always look into the mirror and smile when applying blush. Apply your blush high up on the apples to lift. Keep your apples on the tree and off the ground. If you apply it too low, it will make your face sag down. Also, make sure you do not leave a big yellow gap of skin between your nose and the apple of the cheek. I would say no more than a half inch space between the apple of the cheek and the bridge of the nose without blush. After the blush is applied, use the same brush make sure it's blended to meet the bronzer. This will give a better transition from blush to bronzer, without defined edges. Avoid putting blush anywhere else on the face. Another old technique that I see people doing ever so often is applying blush to the end of their nose like Rudolph the Red Nose Reindeer. I don't get it. You just spent all that time covering the redness on your nose with foundation. Why would you add it back? Let's keep it simple, ladies. Don't try and get too creative.

## Step Three: Highlighter

As you might have already noticed, I like skin with glow. Highlighters are a great way to achieve this look. They can be made of pearl powder, mica, or shimmer in a powder or liquid form. As an artist, I choose to stick with powder formulas because they're easier to blend, and they do not break apart liquid foundation after it's been set by powder. I try to stay away from highlighters with chunky glitter because it looks unnatural. I want my skin to glow without looking like I've been in the glitter aisle of a craft store.

In order to avoid looking like a disco ball, only certain areas should be highlighted. I know we get excited because it looks so pretty, but please do not highlight your entire face. Pick the features that you want to bring forward, and only highlight there. Usually, I start by applying to my T-zone. This is the area above the brows, in the center of the forehead, and down the top of the nose. Another great place to highlight is on top of the cheekbones. Be careful not to get this on the bronzer when applying. Your highlighter should be applied above the edge of the bronzer at the peak of your cheekbone. You can also lightly apply over the blush on the apples to make them glow.

*Please note:*

Not all highlighters look good in photographs or on television. In most cases, the lights and the flash of a camera can make the skin look wet or oily. I am very careful and use highlighter minimally for any photography, and rarely use them for head shots. Again, my formula of foundation already has a glow. You won't need to add a heavy shimmer to get a dewy look.

# Chapter 5
## "Pucker Up"

---

Lipstick, Liner, and Gloss

They say a woman's confidence is in her brows and her bright lips. I am all about a pop of color on the lips. On the other hand, I'm also in love with a creamy nude lip, as long as it is defined and doesn't fade into the face.

There is no one perfect shade for all women. Your perfect shade is determined by your coloring, personality, and style of clothing. When these things change, so will the color choices in your makeup. Just as all other trends change from season to season, lip colors do as well. Just because a color looked great in the 1990's doesn't mean that it looks great today. Plus, you look different than you did 20 years ago. It may be time to retire that mocha brown shade that was the best seller in 1998. The reason why it's so hard to find now is because you are one of the only three people on the planet still wearing it. Honey, it's time to let go. Together, we can do this.

## Selecting the perfect shade:

Just like coordinating your clothing, you should also be doing this with makeup. I like to make sure the lip color matches the cheek color. It's similar to matching your belt with your shoes. This ensures everything flows on your face. If you choose a raspberry lip, you should be wearing a pink/plum based blush, not a shade of coral orange. Otherwise you start to clash and begin to look like you have urban street art on your face. Makeup is meant to enhance, not to look like a grade school art project.

I believe your best color is one you feel comfortable in, that flows with your coloring and features. If you are a red head with fair skin, I definitely would not choose a deep, vamp purple shade for your lips. Just because you saw it on the runway at New York Fashion Week, it doesn't mean it translates well in person for your daily look.

## All day wear:

The rule of thumb for the longest wearing lip products are ones that are matte. Lip pencils, lipsticks, or liquid stains that dry down without a shine are the way to go. Any lip product that is really glossy or hydrating is going to come off the quickest. They tend to slide around, and in turn, you eat them.

I recently started carrying a line of waterproof gel lip liners in a variety of shades to create a matte look. First, I apply a foundation all over my lips to canvas the lip and to mute any natural color in the lips. Next, I set with powder to make sure the lips are dry. Never lick your lips before applying lip colors. Finally, I fill in the entire lip with a shade of the waterproof gel lip liner. Since it is matte, it will stain the lips for 6-8 hours. Of course the lips feel dry, as they should. I don't like that feeling, but who does, so I apply a lip hydrator. The one I carry is called Lip Dew SPF 15. It has avocado oil in it, so it feels much better than the liner worn alone. Once it soaks in you won't see shine, and afterwards the lip liner feels more comfortable on the lips. You can top with a gloss, but keep in mind that by adding the high shine product the stain won't stay on as long.

## Ombre lip:

This is one of my newest tricks. I learned from watching another artist, and it clicked! It was exactly how I would paint lips on a canvas. Why wasn't I already doing this?

Basically, 'Ombre' gives dimension to the lips. Just like ombre highlights for the hair. After you have filled in the entire lip with your choice of color, you then use a shade or two darker in the outer corners. Traditionally, we have used the liner to frame the entire lip. With ombre, you fill in the outer corners in 4 places: both sides of upper and lower lips in triangle shapes, and then shade them in. After you have shaded in the corners of the lip, step back and look at how the lip appears 3D. The illusion of a shadow versus highlight creates dimension so the lips instantly look fuller towards the center. One shade of lipstick or lip liner filled in all over looks flat. To take the ombre a step further, try using an opal, gold, or shimmer gloss in the center of the bottom lip and press the lips together. The reflection of light from the pearl or shimmer creates the illusion that the center part of your lip is coming forward. This really makes the lips pop and look fuller.

## Throw and go:

There is a time and a place to wear high shine glitter and pearl gloss, and it's not in the carpool line to drop off the kids at 7am. Set aside your light color glosses (pale baby pink, light gold, shades of white or cream) and only use these when dressing up, applied over a darker shade of lipstick. Never wear these glosses alone. It isn't very flattering when your lips are whiter than your face. Colors like the ones mentioned above are used to open up the lips, only towards the center of a darker lip to add dimension.

When choosing a shade for quick and easy application, try finding a shade that's an enhancement of your natural lip tone, such as a sheer pink, mauve, or pink beige.  If you aren't wearing a lot of makeup, don't use the brightest gloss in your drawer. It's about looking balanced and believable. Some of us (like myself) don't have a lot of natural color in our lips. By choosing a pink beige, I can achieve a pop so I don't look washed out. To others, it may just look like I have a clear hydrating gloss on. If you are going to fill in your brows, wear heavy liner and mascara, then, by all means use a fluorescent tangerine gloss. Now that would be balancing the act. For an effortless look, bright lips are not as appealing as a neutral shade.

## Basic Application of Traditional Lipstick:

For many years I first applied lip liner around the edge of my lip, then applied my lipstick. Depending on my mood, I would follow my lipstick with a gloss, or would sometimes go without. It was an unsolvable dilemma for me when I would glance in the mirror hours later, only to see the remnants of the lip liner on half my lips. I had eaten off all the lipstick and only a hard chocolate color liner remained. The first problem here was the fact that I even owned a chocolate brown liner. The second issue was my order of application. I'll never forget the VHS Bobbi Brown sent me home with for some at home training. When I got to the part where Bobbi recommended putting lipstick on first, then liner, then gloss, I questioned my ability to show up to work the next day. How could I go against everything I had been teaching women for almost a decade? For the first time I set aside my pride and tried her technique the next day. Damn it, she was right. It all came off at the same time! Who wants their liner to stay on after all the rest if you are strictly lining the edge with a color that doesn't match your lipstick? Nobody. Well, I can think of one group that does this.

She also taught us how to properly match the liner to the lipstick. There isn't a one size fits all shade for liners. Choose a liner that's an enhancement of the lipstick shade you have on, only a couple of shades darker, and match the tone. Brown goes with brown, and red goes with red. Keep it simple, and don't keep trying to make the wrong colors work together.

After applying the lipstick, frame the lips just up to the perioral edge. This is the edge of your lip that frames the shape, right before turning back in towards the face. It's not necessarily where the natural color stops, it's more of the true edge to the lip. You can draw on that edge, but do not go beyond it.

Drawing the liner past the perioral edge looks obvious and is not flattering to others watching you speak. It's distracting, and if I am being brutally honest here, it looks a hot mess. You may think you are fooling others with thick luscious lips, we all know what you are doing here. You didn't fool anyone. It just looks like you can't draw inside the lines. I don't know when or if the McDonald's arches on your upper lip were ever a thing, but please stop. Help me help you. Try lip injections, it looks a lot more believable.

---

# Chapter 6
## "Framing and Canvassing Eyes"

Brows, Brow Lift, and Eye Base

Filling in your eyebrows is one of the most important things you can do with your makeup. Brows frame the face, and without them your eyes just fade into your forehead. Doing them correctly is also extremely important. They say to never trust a woman with bad brows, and it's true.

Full, yet maintained brows give your face a youthful look, while ultra-thin or completely drawn on brows give the look of a hard life. If you have stunted the growth of your brows from over tweezing in your younger years, it's ok. There are many products on the market now that stimulate brow and lash growth. I've used them, and they work!

**There are many factors that go into having flawless brows. Here are some of the items on my eyebrow checklist:**

*1. Do your brows match the darkest part of the hair on your head?*

If you color your hair red, you need to warm up the brows with a red toned brown. If not, you will not look finished. You have to make sure everything coordinates and flows together seamlessly. With this being said, if you are a bleached blonde, please do not put bleach in your eyebrows. I have seen this a few times and it is not flattering. For blondes, your brow should match the darkest part of your hair, which would be the area around your root. I have two shades that I like to use for blondes: Urban Cowgirl or Stonehenge. These are great colors for filling in brows for blondes because they do not have red pigment in them. Most shades of brown turn red when they hit the skin. If you fill in your brows with a brown color and you are a platinum blonde, you will not match. My Blonde Brow Pencil is better for a strawberry blonde, since it has a touch of warmth. If your hair is auburn or dark brown use the corresponding color to match your hair. I never recommend using a pure black pencil or eyeshadow in the brow. If your hair is black, try using a deep brown instead.

*2. Do your inner brows align straight above the inner corner of the eye?*

Have you ever wondered where your brow should start and stop? It's easy. If you were to draw a line straight up from the inner corner of your eye, that should line up to the edge of your inner eyebrow. If your eyebrow comes in closer than this point, we need to find your tweezers. If your brow starts further outward, then we are taking your tweezers away.

*3. Do your brows go up towards the arch and down after?*

Flat brows are unflattering. I realize that some people's brows just grow this way, and this is exactly why we fake it till we make it by filling them in.

Try my technique: I start towards the lower inner corner, draw a baseline going upwards towards the arch, and then downwards after the arch. Even if it's a small arch, at least you have shape to your brow. You can exaggerate the arch by drawing a little further down towards the lower inner corner and a little further up on the outer edge sloping downward. As long as you groom the brow after and set with gel, it will start to look more natural.

*4. Do your brows have a smooth transition from the larger part of the brow to the outer end?*

If you have what I call the quotation brow, I'm talking to you, so keep reading. The arch of your brow should not be towards the inner corner of your brow, closest to your nose. Some women over tweeze the lower inner corner of their brow and create a bubble, with the line off of it. It ends up looking like a comma, or quotation mark, and I can't deal with that. I will fill in the entire lower part of the brow until you can grow it back. We want to smooth the transition from the larger part of your brow all the way to the thinner part of the brow.

Also remember that brows are sisters, not twins. Nobody's brows are the exact same on each side. Sometimes we have to draw a little tail on one to match the other. This is totally normal, and you aren't alone.

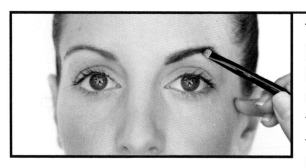

To fill in the brow I use a stiff angled brush with powder, or a powder based pencil to fill in. I'm not a fan of using waxed based pencils because they look too drawn on and are hard to blend. I start towards the lower inner corner of the brow and draw a baseline all the way up towards the top of arch. This line should be intense, and darker than the rest of your natural brow.

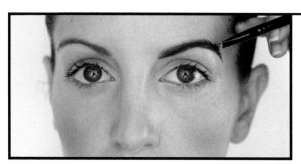

Once I get to the top of the arch, I turn the angle of the brush and go downward to the end of the brow. Make sure you're only filling in the top side of the brow on the second half for more of a lifted look.

Once the baselines are drawn, I soften the color on the brush with a tissue to release some of the pigment. I then go back to where I started and brush the hair in an upward motion, off the baseline and through the rest of the brow. Always brush upwards, because that's the way hair grows and it looks more blended. Plus it makes your brow look a little more lifted.

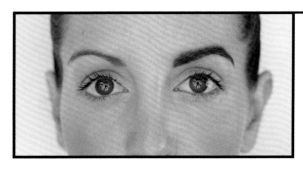

Filling in your brow horizontally leads to a very unnatural, stenciled looking brow. Like you used one of those stencil kits or a Sharpie. If your brows are unruly and tend to want to move in different directions throughout the day, I recommend using a clear brow gel to set the hair in place. I use a brow gel every day on myself and I don't have unruly brows. I choose to use this product because I do not like seeing powder in my brow hair. The clear brow gel gives it a glossy look and makes my brows have a healthier glow.

Whether you use a powder or pencil, it's the same technique. The only difference is that after drawing on your brow with a pencil, I recommend using a softening tool to blend it out. If it's a wax based pencil, it's not going to blend well. If it's a softer powder type pencil, once you blend it should look like real hair.

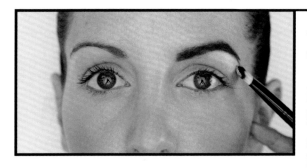

After filling in the brow, I like to use a product that I call the Brow Lift Light. This is by far my number one best-selling item in my entire line. It is a cream-based shadow, without shimmer, that I use with a concealer brush to sharpen up the underside of the brow. I apply this product only to the outer 2/3 of the brow to make you look as if you had a brow lift. By adding a tone lighter than your skin on the brow bone, it creates an opening affect and it literally looks like your eyebrow is sitting up higher on your face.

Not only does it give you a lift, it is also good for hiding any hair that needs to be tweezed. If you were one of those women that gets waxed or threaded, and three days later you can see the hair growing under the skin, this product will be your new best friend. It literally makes it look like you get waxed every day of the week. It is made with beeswax so it reflects the light and looks like skin.

I am not a fan of putting powder shadow underneath the eyebrow. It looks flat and dull. If it's metallic, frosted, or shimmery, it just looks like you are an ornament on the ceiling at a night club. That is actually one of my biggest pet peeves because it looks so unnatural. Wearing Brow Lift alone opens up the eyes and looks so clean and believable. It reflects light and looks creamy so it looks like skin. You won't need to place another product over it.

Before

After

Next, you want to cover the entire lid with an eyeshadow base. Even if you are not going to be wearing an eyeshadow, this product is great for covering redness or veins on the eyelid. It is wheat in color and neutralizes any dark circles on the lid as well. It also acts as a magnet, grabbing your powder shadows and therefore dropping off more pigment. The shadows also blend together easier and stay on longer. It does not contain oil, and is the only thing that you should have between your skin and your eyeshadows.

Once your eyes are framed with flawless brows and your eyelid is prepped and canvased, you are ready for eyeshadow!

IMPACT EYESHADOW

**Kiss Me Cupid**

Ingredients: MICA,
May Contain (+/-):
Carmine,
Titanium Dioxide,

JENTRY KELLEY COSMETICS, HOUSTON, TX

# Chapter 7
## "Eye Spy"

## A basic eye:

For a quick and easy look, try using just two shadow colors. When I am in a hurry, I choose one color for the lid with a little bit of shimmer to enhance my small eyelid. Then, a medium to light matte shade for the crease. I use my large shadow brush to press my first color onto the lid. If you are using my natural eye base, it should grab the pigment quite easily. Applying eyeshadow to the lid in a tapping motion will cause less fall out underneath the eye. Try not to over blend the first color that you apply. Just focus on laying the color onto the eyelid, and do not try and blend the edges yet. After the lid color has been placed, I switch to the blending shadow brush. Rule of thumb: never use a shimmer shadow in the crease of your eye! Remember, matte colors draw things in, while shimmer products reflect light and bring things outward. When it comes to your crease, we always want it to go inward. Using a matte shade in the crease is like SPANX for the eyes! If you use an eyeshadow color with frost or shimmer in the fold of your eye, it will accentuate any lines and wrinkles and make you look older. For those of you with a hooded eye lid, which causes extra skin to hang in the crease, shimmer shadow in the crease is the last thing you need. This also means you should never use a frosted or shimmering shadow as your all over color. The Brow Lift and Eye Base are the only two products that go all the way across your eyelid area. All other colors are pressed into the areas where they belong and are later blended. When the colors are applied directly onto the cream base, it allows them to grab better. If you use Eye Base, then sweep a vanilla colored shadow all the way across your lid, the other shades of eyeshadow that you use will not stay on as well. Powder does not adhere to powder well.

From here, line the upper eyes and apply mascara. Details on application for these two products are mentioned in the next chapter. For an easy day look, don't over think it and use too many shadows. Also keep in mind what type of makeup is appropriate for what time of day. If your clothing is casual, your makeup should be as well. If you don't have a super glamorous job, you probably shouldn't be doing a smoky eye for work. Leave the smoky eye for social events or evening wear.

## Contoured eye:

When I first started applying makeup 20 years ago, we used white eyeliner or white shadow on the lid. Then we would take a dark brown color and buff that through the crease. For a more modern look, I do not use white eyeliner anymore, and neither should you. I prefer to do a light to medium shade all across the lid first. This can be any shade from a soft, pink pearl, to a light caramel. Then choose a matte medium brown shadow and apply to the outer edge of the lid to add closure. When you don't use colors that are so drastically different, it is much easier to blend. You will still be adding shape to your eye and contouring it, but it won't be the late 1990's trend of white versus chocolate brown shadow colors. Use the same matte medium brown and start to buff through the crease going lighter as you go inward. The crease of your eye is the area right above your eyeball and below your brow bone. Sometimes your skin will crease over your eyelid, but that's not your true crease. Pretend like you're sticking a small tight brush in between your eyeball and the brow bone. That's the fold you should be working with. Continue to blend until all colors are married together, and you no longer see defined edges.

## Smokey eye:

I start with a matte or shimmery medium to dark tone on the lid, matte medium color in the crease to blend, then I use my eyeliner. I never start with the really dark black eyeshadow or a deep chocolate. Instead, I do the colors mentioned, apply liner, and then smoke off my eyeliner with a black. After the liner is applied, I use my smoky eye smudge brush with my black shadow and I start smudging around eyeliner a little bit heavier towards the outer portion of the eye and outer c-shape. Once I get all the colors on, I like to use the crease and corner brush to blend in and soften the edges. I call it marrying the colors. It is important to blend all of the colors together. At the very end, to lift some of the darkness, I like to use a loose shimmer shadow pressed with my middle finger on the eyelid over the iris area. This creates an illusion that your eyelid is bigger and coming forward. We used to highlight in the inner corner of the eye, but the more modern technique is to highlight in the center of the lid. This prevents your eyes from looking too far apart, and instead gives more of an enhancement to the natural shape of the eye.

After applying heavier eye makeup, you may end up with drop off. This is powder that has fallen down while you were working. To avoid heavy drop off, try tapping your brush on the edge of the counter to the remove excess powder. Also tap and press the color over the Eye Base so it grabs, without flicking your brush back-and-forth. Somehow, someway, I always end up dropping a little dark shadow onto my concealer. Use a fan brush (mine is called the Clean Sweep brush) to dust off any excess powder first. If there is excessive drop-off, use a Q-tip with an eye serum or an eye cream and twist over the area that has the dark shadow. The cream on the Q-tip should lift up the dark color. For a really clean and crisp look at the very end, I always go back over with either and under eye brightener or my concealer. This will sharpen up the bottom part of your eye if you used any shadow to frame the lower lash line, and it will also erase any eyeshadow that you got too far past the edge of your brow.

I tend to avoid using a lot of color with eyeshadows. I will still work with deep plums, cranberries and wine shades, and taupe/olive green. I just don't like to use turquoise, lime green, or hot pink to add color to the eye area. I prefer to keep it simple and natural and get my pops of color on the lips and cheeks instead. If you want to add a little hint of color around the eye area, start by using neutral shadows, then line your eyes and use a really tight brush to add the bright colors only against the lash line over your eyeliner. This will keep people looking a just little closer, without making you look like a wall of graffiti.

# Chapter 8

## "The Bottom Line"

---

Application of Eyeliner and Mascara.

I have to devote an entire chapter for these two steps: eyeliner and mascara. It's a subject I often bring up on social media, and something I have to fully explain in detail to every client who sits in my chair.

First, I will explain my eyeliner and mascara techniques, and then I will back it up with several photos. You may not agree at first, but keep reading. I challenge you to take a step back from the mirror and compare. Take your own before and after photos, and even ask friends. They probably just don't know how to tell you to lay off the bottom eyeliner. But I'm not scared to tell you the truth. I mean, it is my purpose here on earth, and I won't stop until all women are free of harsh drawn on black bottom eyeliner. This will be the day that planet Earth will become the most beautiful place in the universe.

Bottom eyeliner is a very sensitive subject for many women. A select few have even become aggressive when I tell them my opinion, mostly on social media. What I find so funny is, as I am teaching lessons in person,

I RARELY get resistance while I am demonstrating this on their face. In person, they can actually see what I am talking about and nearly every single time, they agree.  But that is also the nature of the internet. Some love to defend the honor of their hard, unblended liquid or pencil eyeliner on the lower lash line and speak loudly about their choice to use it. Keep on, girl... we are all over here looking 5-10 years younger and more modern without bottom liner.

I know bottom eyeliner addiction is hard to get past, but together we can get through this. I wore it once upon a time as well, so I know how you are feeling. Just sit back, relax, and stay open minded while reading this chapter. This could be life changing for you, or you can leave this lesson with the same habits you have had since 2003. The women who have since seen the light have thanked me for showing them how to look younger and more lifted. Many have even said they thought I was full of it, but still gave the NO BOTTOM EYELINER challenge a try. Now they never wear bottom eyeliner, and look back at old photos and cringe. After you read this, you will probably start to notice this unflattering makeup technique on others and will find it hard to concentrate when that person speaks to you. I know the feeling. Imagine how I feel.

I love a defined upper lid and a winged cat liner when done properly. For myself, I use a black cake liner with a damp flat brush to make me look alive. I call it Watercolor Eyeliner. If you have experience painting with watercolor, it's the same concept. The brush has to be damp to allow pigment to transfer. It won't move if used dry, and even though it looks like eyeshadow, it's not. Once the brush is lightly dampened, I work into the compact of liner until I achieve a texture similar to shoe polish. I press and wiggle starting at the base of my lash from the underside. Then, to get a more defined look, I also apply the liner into the lash line from the top side (which is optional). This gives me a solid lash line, making my lashes look twice as thick. When complete, you can no longer see any pink skin between the lashes. I go from the outer corner and complete the line to the inner corner. I never stop halfway because it looks unfinished.

Please do not become a 1/2 way eyeliner offender. It looks like the phone rang, and you forgot what you were doing. I do, in fact, taper it off and go thinner as I go in. All of this is on the upper lid only. The how-to video on YouTube is so important if this is a technique you haven't tried. For the easiest application, you must hold your chin up and look down into a mirror. If you don't own one of those table top mirrors that tilt, you need to head to TJMAXX asap. This way, you can work with your eyes open instead of squinting to see what you are doing in a wall mirror. I move my face from the left to the right when I apply the liner to avoid going directly over the iris. I'm a flincher, so I don't like the brush to go directly over my eyeball while I'm working.

Here is the part women struggle with. I don't recommend applying eyeliner to the lower lash line. Eyeliner only goes on the upper lash line. This is the exact reason why I don't sell a pencil liner in my makeup line. It's shocking to me how many women still apply their eyeliner with a liquid or pencil on the lower lash line and don't even attempt to blend. It weighs the eye down and makes you look older. Plus, that look is outdated. Instead, if needed, I apply a bronze or a light to medium color eyeshadow into the lower lash line to ween someone off the lower liner habit. It looks soft and smokey versus hard and defined. Some women say to me, "But I am different, I HAVE to wear bottom eyeliner." I have never met a women that NEEDED bottom eyeliner, and I have done makeup on thousands of people. You may think you look silly or sick without it, but it's just your comfort zone. Also, I don't recommend using any type of liner on the waterline on the lower rim. This means no white eyeliner either. As a matter of fact, if you still own a white eyeliner, it may need to be retired. Tonight would actually be a great time to dispose of that.

Notice in the next photo how the eye on the left side of photo appears as if it's sitting lower on the face. That side has unblended pencil eyeliner on the bottom.

Adding weight to the bottom of the eye with a black, navy, or deep brown color will drag the eye down. Again, it's the law of color I have mentioned before. Darker will add weight, and lighter/brighter will lift. Look at the right side of photo where I do not use a pencil or liquid liner on the bottom. I only use a light bronze eyeshadow to frame. That eye looks like it's sitting an inch higher on the face! Now do I have your attention?

Wearing heavy bottom liner weighs the eye down, making you look tired. Also, it's very distracting when it's the ONLY thing you use on your eye. I've heard a woman say before, "I'm just lazy, so to look awake I only use bottom eyeliner before I leave the house." That is so far from the truth! You are doing the exact opposite of waking up your eyes when you wear bottom eyeliner.

Now let's discuss mascara. While we are on the subject of the lower lash line, I guess now is the time to mention I don't like mascara on the bottom either. It's the same concept of adding something dark and pulling the eye downward. Especially since the hair grows downward, by extending the lashes it's pulling it down that much further. I have heard some women say, "But I'm a blonde, you can't see my lashes on the bottom." GOOD! You are one of the lucky ones. You don't want to see them on the bottom. Let's keep it that way.

The basics of mascara application are pretty self-explanatory. Always curl the lashes BEFORE mascara. Curling the lashes after mascara can cause them to stick to your lash curler and pull them out. Apply mascara as the very last step on the eyes, after eyeshadows and eyeliner. If mascara is applied first, eyeshadow builds up over the mascara and causes them to appear chalky. For a fresher look, make sure it's the last thing you do.

When choosing mascaras, I try to avoid formulas that contain fibers. For a short period of time there was a craze over this two-step process of applying fibers and mascara, then repeating two more times. Of course I tried it, because I'm willing to try anything once, but it did not work for me. It looked similar to the photo below.

It made my lashes look sloppy, clumpy, and throughout the night I had little fibers falling on my upper cheekbone area. I gave it three shots, and even watched a how to video from the company, but for me they just did not work. It's much easier to apply a set of false lashes for a fuller look, then coat with mascara to finish it off. False lashes also look more whispy, and less clumpy than this technique.

As far as the style and thickness of a mascara wand, it's personal preference. I actually prefer a traditional shaped mascara wand. I like my wand to have a stiffer spoolie, which makes for better lash separation.

I think some of the newer style rubber wands tend to grab too much mascara, and are harder to work with. When I apply the mascara, I start towards the center of the lash line at the base. I wiggle the wand from the base of the lash to the end of the lash, pulling upward, as I twist it in my fingers. This ensures that you're coating the entire hair and not just the tip, and separating the lashes at the same time. Then, on the outer edge, I start from the base and pull towards the hairline near the ear. This will give more of a fanned out look and extend the lashes on the outer edge. Towards the inner part of the eye I use the tip of the wand to twist, and pull towards the nose. This will help the inner corner stand up to look a bit longer.

When it comes to shades of mascara, I keep it simple. Black is best for almost every tone of skin and hair color. Brown or burgundy mascara can make the eyes look red and tired. Mascara should make your eyes pop! Brown puts most eyes to sleep. The only time I would pick up a brown mascara would be for a porcelain skin tone with red hair. It flows with this coloring really well, but not so much on all other tones. I do like a blue mascara, but it's not for everybody. Choose a blue mascara that has a nice black base to it. I would recommend using this shade for someone with lighter eyes (either green or blue) and lighter hair. It makes those eye colors pop. Most people won't even notice it's the mascara that's blue. They will think your eyes that changed color. If you have dark brown hair and colored eyes, the blue mascara doesn't really give you the depth that you need and you can end up looking washed out.

For a natural look during the day, I only recommend using one coat of mascara. Dramatic lashes with a natural makeup application looks unbalanced and is very distracting. People can only focus on your lashes, and hear less of what you are saying. When eyeshadow and eyeliner are applied, I recommend adding a second coat after the mascara dries. For a heavy smoky eye, I also recommend applying heavier mascara or false strip lashes to step up the look. See my YouTube channel for a video on false lash application.

One question I get often is, "How often should you replace your mascara?" According to therapeutic optometrist Dr. Sheena Garner, you should replace your mascara every 90 days. "Most patients are quick to blame something or someone for their pink eye," says Dr. Garner. "Doctors, on the other hand assume that the patient is over wearing their contacts, coming down with a cold, or were recently in contact with someone with a similar infection. In reality, many of these eye infections come from conjunctivitis and extended use of cosmetics (or sharing cosmetics), particularly mascara." I always try to tell my clients to never share their makeup, but they don't always listen. This goes for brushes and your makeup products. Usually, your ears don't perk up until your doctor determines that this is the reason why you got your eye infection and you then have to throw away all of your eye makeup. It's gross, expensive, and not to mention frustrating when you have to buy all new makeup. Dr. Garner adds, "Every time someone uses mascara, the microbial exposure is multiplied. The most common offenders for allergic or bacterial infections are from Demodex, better known as lash mites." I know it's gross, but I have to be the one to break the bad news. You have bugs that live in your eyelashes.

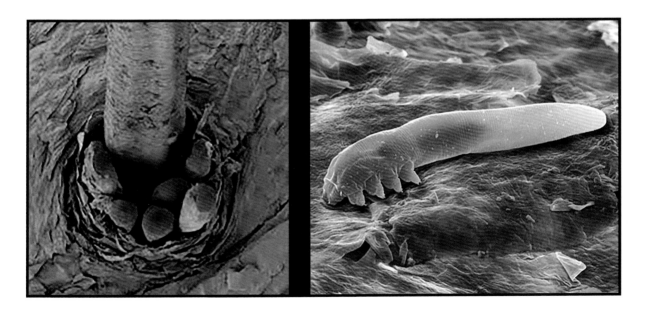

They lay eggs on your hair follicles and when their eggs hatch, they feed on them. This can lead to itchy eyelids, inflammation, or flaking around the lash line. By sharing your mascara with somebody else, you are sharing your bugs with theirs. As a makeup artist, I never double dip my mascara wand and I always use disposable ones. It doesn't mean that you need to use disposable wands for your personal use. Buying the disposable wands is more expensive than a new tube of mascara. Just make sure you're not cross contaminating and sharing with others and that you replace it every 90 days, even if you still have some left in the tube. If you've been hoarding 14 tubes of mascara in your drawer in case of an emergency, those need to go in the trash as well. Once opened and used, even if it's only once, the expiration is 90 days. If you need to use a marker to write the date on it from when it was opened, do it. Stay on track with replacement tubes to prevent an overabundance of these lash mites.

Little by little, I have had women stop using bottom eyeliner and mascara who then praise me for having helped them see the light. I feel like I have to be very direct when teaching this part of the lesson because there will always be a fighter that thinks they are the exception to the rule. I have never come across a face that needed bottom liner, or looked silly without it. It's a bad habit that's hard to break. After about a week of seeing yourself without it, you get used it. After about a week you will see what I am talking about. People will also start complimenting your makeup, and will sometimes think that you must have had some Botox because you look more lifted. If you are a bottom liner offender, I challenge you to stop today and give it a whole week. I bet by the end of the week your mind will start to change. At least I pray it does.

# Chapter 9
## "Cute in Carpool"

3-5 Minute Makeover for Women on the Go.

Several years ago, one of my favorite clients, Sheri Bailey came to me and said, "I love when you do my makeup for events, but for every day I won't do all 20 steps. I have three kids, and I need something quick and easy. Show me what I can do in five minutes or less, because I just need to look cute in the carpool line." I sat her down and showed her the eight items I thought all women should never leave the house without.

It was easy to learn, quick to apply, and made her look bright and awake without looking like she had tried. This is when my 3-5 minute, eight step makeover came to life. Conveniently, I named it "Cute in Carpool". Let's give Sheri a round of applause for allowing me to come up with this genius idea, and for giving other women an easy system that actually works!

You don't have to be a mom to use it. The name implies it's for women who do carpool, but this is really for everyone. I don't have kids and I do it five out of seven days a week. Call it "Cute in College" if you are a student, "Cute in the Courtroom" if you are an attorney, or "Cute in Clinic" if you are in the medical field. Whatever you want to call it. I just call it easy. If you have the life of a teacher or nurse and have to be up at 5am to start your day, it's a super-fast routine that you can do when you don't have 30 minutes to spare for makeup application. It's about looking bright and awake and not like you just rolled out of bed.

One can also customize "Cute in Carpool" into a routine they feel most confident in. It's just a recommendation on where to start. Personally, I like to add brows to the eight steps because I look as if I was burned in a fire without them. Plus, I like extra coverage on my skin so I always add a foundation as well. So, my eight steps has turned into 10 but still takes me less than five minutes to apply. I'm fast though, because well, it's my job to be! Don't get frustrated in the beginning because it took you 10 minutes. Each time you will get better and faster until you have it down to five minutes. Once you master it, you won't even think twice about the 3-5 minutes it takes you to apply it. It will be as natural to you as brushing and flossing your teeth.

In the previous chapters, I explained the details of application with each product. Below is a summary of those details, a list of the products I use, and why they are important to get the finished result.

## Step One:
## Tinted Primer SPF 20

I always say if you're going to put sunscreen on, you might as well choose one that has some coverage in it as well. I combined a primer, tinted moisturizer, and SPF all-in-one for a quick, easy application. If you're trying to be fast, you need to start combining things that work well together. This product has a sheer overall coverage, which tones down redness. This is what makes our face look tired. If you put on a full coverage, heavy mask of foundation with very natural makeup in all the other categories, it doesn't look balanced. This product is sheer and still looks like skin, just more polished with a glow. Remember to avoid putting this product in the eye socket area. It will look cakey under the eye and crease on your eyelid.

## Step Two:
## Concealer

Never, I repeat, never leave the house without under-eye concealer on. I don't care how rested you think you look, we all need concealer. For the not so fortunate ones who got only three hours of sleep, this is how you fake it till you make it. You will look as if you got eight hours every night if done properly. It's also the one step where women come back to me saying it doesn't look the same when they apply it on their own. When I watch how they apply their makeup, the common mistake is how little they are using. Women tend to underuse concealer. Keep going! Keep adding until you think you have enough, and then add some more. When you look like you have 15lbs of it under your eye, you can stop. The trick to making concealer look like skin is to warm it up with your fingers and texturize it by pressing it in. Once you set it in with powder, it brightens your day and your under eyes as well.

## Step Three:
## Powder

You can't put liquid products on your face without setting them with powder. Well, unless you want it all over your cell phone and on your kid's clothing when you hugged him off to school. Liquid makeup will transfer if it's not set with powder properly. If you aren't a fan of heavy face powder, try a translucent powder. If you are like me and like a little extra coverage, try a medium coverage face powder to add a little bit more coverage than the primer gives alone. I avoid using sponges to apply the powder, and instead dust a small amount with the fan brush. Use just enough powder to where you don't feel it stick to your skin when you press your hand against your face. Also, make sure you dust the under eye concealer to set it as well.

## Step Four:
## Bronzer

There are three basic products to use on the cheek: blush, bronzer, and highlighter. Many of you may think blush is the most important thing, but this is incorrect. When you're in a hurry and you only have five minutes to do your makeup, warm your face up with a bronzer and skip the blush. Especially if you have the white neck syndrome that I wrote about earlier. It's more important to make sure all the colors flow together from your chest to your face. Even more than a pop of rosy tone on your apples. By applying the bronzer to your face and neck, not only are you taking five pounds off by shading, you are also giving dimension to the face so it doesn't look flat. If you find you have extra time at the very end, then you can add blush.  Try the full eight steps of "Cute in Carpool" first, before making that decision. I bet you won't even feel like you need it. I skip the highlighter step altogether for "Cute in Carpool." Remember that this is only a summary of the entire makeup routine, not every piece of makeup you have in your drawer applied to your face at once.

## Step Five:
## Lip Gloss

If you want to keep the makeover under five minutes, you won't have time to do lipstick, liner, and gloss. Keep it simple and try to find a color of lip-gloss that is an enhancement of your natural lip and gives you a little color. Avoid the creamy nude shades that are lighter than your skin tone, heavy shimmer, or yellow gold tones. Those tones of lip-gloss look better over darker lipsticks, and when worn alone they wash out the face and look like death, or like a hooker. The colors from my line that I like best are Hibiscus, Sweet Nothings, Ginger Rose, Terra-cotta Twist, or any other shade that is an enhancement of your natural lip color. I also try to avoid electric pinks or tangerine shades for this look. It looks unbalanced if everything else is soft, and then you are rocking a bold lip. If you are not a fan of lip-gloss, as an alternative, you can choose a lipstick instead, like Princess or Brown Sugar.

## Step Six:
## Brow Lift Light

This is by far the very best thing that I've created for my line. It's my number one seller, and there's a reason for that. Mostly because it gives you five years of your life back. But it also opens up the eyes and wakes the face up. It is a cream-based product made of beeswax that is to be applied to the outer two thirds of your eyebrow. It creates an illusion of light making you look as if the outer side of your eyebrow is being pulled upward. It looks more like skin than a white powdered shadow underneath the brow because it's light reflective. Avoid putting it all the way across the eye because that will flatten the brow line. It also gives more definition to the underside of the brow, making you look as if you have been threaded or waxed, and conceals any little hair that is growing in. When you don't have time to apply eye shadow and liner, this product gives a smooth clean look to the eye.

## Step Seven:
## Eye Base Natural

This is the alternative to putting concealer or foundation on your eyelid. As mentioned before, and I will say it five more times, please do not apply foundation to the eyelids. Also, make sure that when you're putting on your facial moisturizers you are not applying them to your eyelids before this product. Any items with oil will cause them to slide around. It is formulated the same as the Brow Lift Light, but instead more of a wheat shade for your lid. If blended properly, you will not be able to see the transition between the Brow Lift and Eye Base. If you use one shade all over, the eye will look flat. We want the eyes to look flawless, yet 3D. Also, the tone of the Eye Base neutralizes veins and redness on the eyelid better than any other shade.

## Step Eight:
## Mascara

You can't go this far and just stop. Mascara is one of the most important steps to wake up the eye area. It's almost like it brings us to life. While applying powder to the skin, some of the dust lands on the eyelashes and makes them look chalky. I always recommend to curl the lashes first, then apply a sheer coat of fiber free mascara. It makes the whole look complete. Avoid putting multiple layers of mascara on for this look. Again, we want to look balanced and appropriate or daytime. Remember, keep that mascara off of the lower lash line. Don't even try it sister! Just like that you're done, Voilà!

## Carpool to Cocktails:

The best thing about "Cute in Carpool" is that it lasts all day. If you decide you want to go out for cocktail hour, just define your brows if needed, add some eyeliner, and pop up the color on your lips and cheeks. You will not have to take everything off and start over. Adding just three to four more steps will give you a more polished look in intimate lighting.

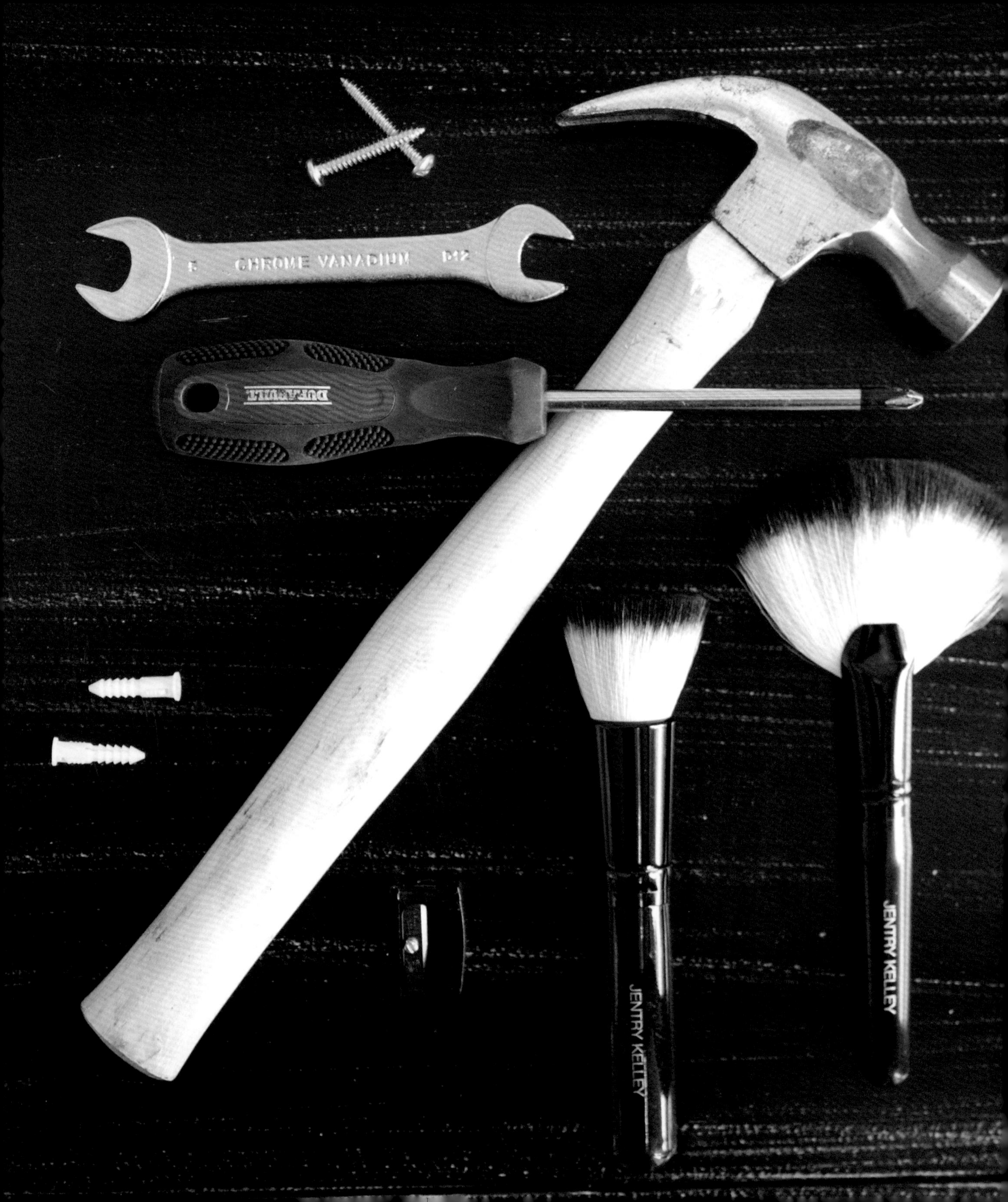
CHROME VANADIUM
JENTRY KELLEY
JENTRY KELLEY

# Chapter 10
## "A Makeup Artist's Tool Box"

---

The tools that make you a master.

Having the correct tools in your kit is imperative to having a flawless face. What is a carpenter without his saw, or a plumber without his wrench? It is also important to fully understand how each tool should be used, and the techniques we use with each one of them. I think it is important to show photos as a reference so you can search through your current tools to see what works best for each category.

## Sponges and Beauty Blenders:

About 8-10 years ago, I retired all of my makeup sponges and I haven't missed them since. At first, it wasn't purposeful. The department store I worked for had run out of sponges and I was forced to use a foundation brush for a week until we received more. By the end of the week, I was so hooked on a brush that I never went back to a sponge. I just had to learn how to use the brush by trial and error until I got it right. Before this, I had never been able to achieve a flawless look like I felt I could get with a sponge. Now I feel my application of foundation looks 100 times better with a brush than it did with a sponge. Plus, sponges absorb so much liquid foundation making you zip through the bottle in half the time. At the end of the week, when you throw your sponge wedge away, so much foundation goes in the trash can with it. This is your hard earned money being thrown away, ladies! Also, if you're not consistently changing out your sponge, you are reapplying bacteria to your face from the days prior. This applies to both liquid makeup and compact powder. Dirty sponges can lead to blemishes and acne.

Compacts are notorious for being a petri dish of bacteria. At the end of the day, when you're touching up your powder and using the sponge that comes with it, you are pulling any bacteria, dirt, and oil off your face and sticking it back in the compact to grab more powder. When you are finished, you set the sponge loaded with oil and bacteria on top of the face powder, and you close the compact. The next day, you end up putting that sponge back onto your face with yesterday's bacteria all over it. Not only do they smell bad, sponges are in a dark, moist place for the bacteria to grow. In just a few weeks, you may notice that the powder is starting to harden in areas with dark shiny bumps. This is your oil and bacteria hardened inside of the powder. So, not only does the sponge steal your expensive liquid makeup, it leaves behind bacteria that hardens in your compact, making your skin prone to breakout. This doesn't sound like a good relationship. I say the sooner you break up with your sponge, the better. Instead, try using a kabuki brush. These are small, and much easier to clean.

## Washing Brushes:

So many women have said to me that they didn't even know you were supposed to wash your makeup brushes. Ekkkkkkkk! This makes me want to beat them with their makeup brush right in the middle of my store. Instead, I try to compose myself, take deep breaths, and tell them about what I call the first Sunday of every month. The official "Brush Wash Day." This way, they never have an excuse for getting off track again. Keeping the brushes hydrated and cleansed will prolong the life of the brush and keep them from contaminating your makeup.

There are two basic types of brush cleansers: one that contains alcohol for makeup artists to use between clients for sanitation purposes, and the other for you to use at home on your own brushes. Makeup artists should be using a brush wash with alcohol to prevent spreading germs from one client to the next. These are usually spray cleansers that not only take out the color, but also help kill germs. The alcohol allows the hair to dry quickly for the next client. The downside to using a spray cleaner with alcohol is that it is really hard on your brushes. As an artist, we have to replace our brushes about once every year or two. The alcohol and the acrylic that the hair is glued in with are not compatible and cause breakage at the base. They also eat away at the paint on the handle of the brush. Instead of an alcohol-based cleanser on your personal brushes, try using a hydrating brush wash. I recommend finding something made specifically for brushes. Avoid using products like baby shampoo, hand soap, and antibacterial dish detergent. These products are not formulated to remove makeup and will not fully clean your brushes. They may also contain alcohol and cause the brush hair to dry out and snap off. A few years ago, I had a chemist formulate my Hydrating Brush Cleanser with a rich lather that removes makeup from the brushes, hydrates the hair with peppermint oil, and leaves the brushes smelling fabulous. I recommend lightly dampening the brush with water and using the cleanser in the palm of your hand. Rotate the brush in a circular motion without mashing the hair down. Foundation and concealer brushes hold onto the pigment the most, so you may need to use less water, more cleanser, and rinse 2-3 times to remove all makeup. Always lay the brushes flat to dry overnight. Never wrap them in a towel or leave submerged in water. They will begin to smell like mildewed wet towels that you left in the washing machine for three days. Also, make sure you squeeze any excess water out for faster drying time. Repeat once a month and you will feel like you have a new set of brushes each time.

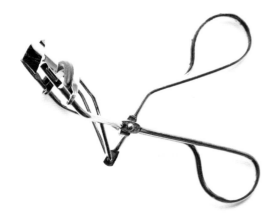

## Lash curler:

I have a strong relationship with my lash curler. I cannot apply mascara without it. Unfortunately, each eyelash that comes out of my lid grows in a different direction. Actually, every direction except for upward. If you

have lashes that grow downward (I find this mostly in Hispanic, Native American, and Asian women), I highly recommend using a curler to open the eyes. It's a myth that all curlers pull out the lashes or pinch the skin, but they can if you are using them incorrectly. In my experience, the traditionally shaped drugstore brand curlers have caused pinching in the corners. I currently use the Laura Mercier curler, which doesn't have sides like a traditional curler does, so I don't have an issue with the pinching. As far as the myth about all eyelash curlers cutting off lashes, this is not true. This happens when the rubber or sponge pad has never been replaced or wears down. At this point, the curler becomes a pair of scissors with metal on metal as you press down. I have also watched other women use lash curlers, and I see them squeeze with all their might. I do not recommend this technique. If it's a good curler, there is no need for this. Also, do not use a curler after you have applied mascara. If the mascara sticks to the curler and you pull it away from your eye, the lashes are coming with it. I have also seen women use a spoon to curl the lashes, but I looked like I had issues with my motor skills when I attempted it. So, I quickly gave up and never tried that again.

## Tweezers:

Every woman should carry a pair of these in her purse, and a second pair at home. Have you ever tried tweezing in the car (in a parking lot of course) with the sun out? Man, you can see every bit of peach fuzz! I always try to face a window or walk outside for tweezing. Always make sure your tweezers are sharpened for the best result. I purchase from Tweezerman and get free sharpening for life. Now that's customer service.

The women who should be grounded from their tweezers are the ones mentioned in the next chapter. If you get obsessed in the mirror and keep going because you can't seem to find a stopping point and end up with pencil thin brows, you are one of these women. Try going in monthly to be threaded by a professional so you can keep a flawless shape that doesn't look overdone.

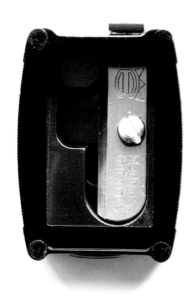

## Pencil Sharpener:

It wasn't until about three years ago that I realized why some sharpeners ate up certain pencils. If your pencil says "Made in Germany" on the handle, your sharpener should say "Made in Germany" on the blade. "Made in China", goes with "Made in China." When you switch those up, you tend to have issues with the sharpeners grinding down your pencil. Also, make sure you replace your sharpener when the blade gets dull.

## Brushes:

**Primer + Foundation-** I only prefer a traditional shaped foundation brush made of synthetic hair. Brushes made of real hair don't seem to work well with things that are creamy. Liquid foundations tend to clump the bristles made of natural hair. I choose to use synthetic because the foundation just sits on the surface instead of being absorbed into the brush. I first apply my primer with this brush, then the foundation. No need to clean in between. I use the back of my hand as a pallet, and use the foundation brush to grab only what I need, as I need it. I swipe to sheer the liquid makeup, twist to fill in the pores around the nose, and tap the flat side of the brush over any area that needs more coverage. If you have redness in the skin, I highly recommend using a brush because the warmth of applying with fingers to the face can cause friction and make the skin turn even more red.

**Brow Lift + Concealer-** This brush should be made of the same material as the foundation brush. Since your concealer is also creamy, I prefer synthetic as well. I like my concealer brush to be about 1/3 of the size of the foundation brush for more precision. You can also use this brush with other makeup products that are creamy in texture. I use this type of brush for three items every day: Concealer, Eyebrow Lift, and Eye Base. I just make sure I tissue the brush off between uses. It's nice to have one brush that you can use with multiple products.

**Powder-** Any time that I use powder-based products, I use brushes made of real hair. Look for brushes made of goat, pony, squirrel, sable, or badger hair. The rule of thumb with brushes is the softer the hair, the softer the application. The harder and stiffer the hair, the more product it's going to pick up and place on your skin. I like to use a medium texture brush made of badger hair, and apply powder in a circular motion to lightly buff into the skin. This will also help get between the hair on your face for more flawless finish.

**Clean Sweep-** This is a multi-purpose brush. It was originally intended to dust off eyeshadow drop off during the clean up process. I have since been using it to apply powder. The fan shape glides across the face seamlessly, while lightly applying powder to set foundation. This one is definitely a customer favorite.

**Kabuki-** A densely packed rounded brush with a very short stem used to apply powder. I enjoy this brush for powder applications on the go, mostly because it doesn't take up much room in the makeup bag. The brush got it's name from Japanese actors who would use this type of brush to apply white face powder in theaters.

**Sheer Buffing-** My favorite brush to apply bronzer with is a goat hair and synthetic blend. These are most commonly designed with black goat hair at the base, with little white synthetic hair springing past it towards the center. I preferred this type brush for someone who is just learning how to apply makeup, or for someone who has fair skin. The dark goat hair grabs the product, and the white synthetic hair buffs it in for a flawless application. I also like this type of brush for highlighter application. If you use a brush with densely packed hair to apply something with shimmer, it tends to look really cakey and obvious on the skin. Whichever option you choose to use this brush for is fine, just don't use it for both. If you mix multiple products on one brush your highlighter will look muddy, and your bronzer will be shimmery from cross-use.

**Flat Contour-** This is a great brush because of the shape and size for shading the cheeks and neck. When using a bronzer with a large powder brush, you tend to over apply and don't get much precision. If you shade with a tight small angled brush, it ends up looking too drawn on and sharp. I use the flat contour brush to lay the color on and below the cheekbone, going back-and-forth from the ear to the nose until it's well blended. I also like to use this brush on the neck to create the neck lift. Most other brushes leave the striped look on the neck, but this brush allows for easy blending.

**Blush-** For this one, I like to pay close attention to size. Blush should only be applied to the apple of the cheek. Choose a brush head more towards the smaller size for precision. I like to use an angled blush brush so only the tops of the apples are hit with the brush. Blush brushes with tapered flat heads also work well. Softly use the flat side of the brush on top of the apples and blend into the edge of the bronzer.

**Angled Brow-** When filling in the eyebrows, you 100% need an angled brush. The stiffer the hair, the better. Angled brushes with soft hair are meant more for winged eyeliner. The stiffer the hair, the better it will blend and come through the brow giving a softer look.

### Large Shadow-

I don't believe in using an all over eyeshadow color. If you are using an eye shadow base, there is no need for that anyway. Instead, I use a large shadow brush to apply eyeshadow only onto the lid. I gently lay the flat side of this brush on the eyeshadow, and swipe back and forth a few times. Then, I use this brush to pat the eyeshadow onto the lid (instead of swiping) to avoid fall out onto the lower eye area. This brush also allows for heavy pigment drop off for true color.

### Blending Shadow-

This type brush has been traditionally called a ponytail brush because of its shape. I believe it is the best brush to use in the crease to blend. I don't like seeing hard lines between the lid and eyebrow, and this brush allows for a smooth gradient effect from light to dark. I never recommend using synthetic hair for eyeshadows, especially in the crease. Brushes made of real hair can give the smoothest application if used correctly. I tuck this brush between the eyeball and the brow bone going back and forth until all colors are blended. It picks up very little pigment, and places very little pigment, which makes for easier blending.

### Crease + Corner-

To reach tighter areas I like to use this brush. When I want to use a darker shade like a black or a rich brown, I use the pointed end of this brush to accentuate the crease and the corner. After the rich pigment has been laid, I go back with the Blending Eyeshadow brush to soften the look. This brush can also be used with the bronze or platinum eyeshadow to frame the lower lash line instead of using eyeliner for a smokey look.

### Smokey Eye Smudge-
This is one of my favorite brushes, and one I could never live without. After I have applied eyeliner on the top lash line, I use this brush with a dark shadow to blend in and soften the edge. It has a real tight, rounded head to allow for precise application. I can also use this brush to frame the lower lash line with eyeshadow. It's a good corrector tool for blending if you try doing your winged eyeliner and didn't get it even. This smudging tool can be a quick, instant fix, and make it look like a makeup artist applied your makeup.

### Watercolor Eyeliner-
This is a synthetic brush used to apply cake liners. This brush must be dampened before working it into the compact of cake eyeliner. The bristles are laid really close together to achieve a tight line used to apply liner underneath the lashes on the waterline. Press and wiggle at the base of the lash to dispense the color.

### Lip-
Honestly, I don't see much use for this brush unless you're a makeup artist. The only time I use a lip brush for personal use is when I'm using lipsticks that have been melted into a compact. This is a great tool to apply lipstick to other people, but not really needed for use on yourself. I once had an artist named Giddony show me a really cool trick with a retractable lip brush. When going out and carrying a small purse without room for lipstick and gloss, try applying your lipstick and gloss to the lip brush and closing the lid. When it's time for touch up you can grab just what's on the brush instead of bringing the two products with you. I thought that was such a great space saving idea!

*Please note:* Do not ever share your personal makeup brushes or tools with another person, unless cleaned properly. This can lead to the spread of the herpes virus, eye infections, and other illnesses.

# Chapter 11

## "What-Not-To-Do"

WARNING! The following chapter is intended for mature and strong audiences. If you need a little liquid courage to get through this part, now is the time to pour yourself a stiff one.

Makeup is just like fashion, trends often change. So many women out there are still using the same makeup techniques they have been doing since high school. Twenty years later, are you wearing the same clothing style you wore back then? If not, why are you still doing the same makeup routine? If so, then you need to just put this book down and move on. I can't help you any further.

Here, I will get you updated. I'll help you drop your old makeup habits, while carrying you into the current decade. It may come as a shock to see some of the things that you do with your own makeup on my "what-not-to-do" list. I understand that old habits die hard, but I am here to beat you with my makeup brush if you refuse to listen and continue to do the things mentioned below. I have confidence in you. You should have confidence in yourself. I am not saying it will be easy for you to let go of all items mentioned below at once. At first, you may hate your new routine with my suggestions, but why not at least try it! Sheeeeeit, you made it this far reading my book, what's a week without bottom eyeliner?

# Here we go!

White Undereye Concealer- Your concealer should be brighter, not whiter than your skin tone. If you see yourself looking like the photo below, you are exactly who I am talking to. You just look like you are trying to cover something up. Try warming it up by choosing a concealer with a pink or peach tone.

Applying Concealer on the Eyelids- This is the sure-fire way to get your eyeshadow to melt and crease by lunchtime! It creates an oil slick on your lid, and when you blink it creases your eyeshadow. By the end of the day, all of your shadow and liner is in a pool of mud. This is why artists have created an eyeshadow base to use instead.

White Face Syndrome- I know you don't do this on purpose. Well, I hope not. I understand that in some cultures, creating a lighter skin tone is considered beautiful, but this is not what I am talking about here. This part is for the ladies who wear their winter shade of foundation in August. When a photograph is taken with the flash... BOO! Ghost face appears. Wardrobe your makeup to the season. When you get a tan, your foundation color needs to change. Match your foundation to your chest. If you don't tan your face, you have to fake it with makeup so you can stay consistent with your body.

Matte Foundations- Skin should look like skin. Dry matte foundations don't look believable. They also make your skin look old by enhancing lines and wrinkles. Stay away from wearing foundation powders to avoid this look.

Foundation on the Neck- Never apply liquid makeup to the neck, unless you want to wear it on your clothing. In natural sunlight, everyone can see the makeup on your neck as it settles in the horizontal lines. Foundation should stop at the jawline, and bronzer should be applied later to warm up the neck. It's a lot more subtle and you can see your skin through it.

"Baking" and Extreme Highlighting- Do you know what this looks like when you walk outside? Please keep these techniques for on-stage makeup. Unless you are an actor, dancer, or drag queen, this technique of highlighting is not for you. If you don't know what baking means, just ignore this, you don't need to know.

Extreme Contouring- These words are completely overused. Cosmetic companies sure did cash in though! All women suddenly wanted to look like something they just were not: to be carved and chiseled like Kim Kardashian. Instead, we now have a bunch of naturally beautiful women walking around looking like they were beat in a back alley. My least favorite makeup trend is using foundations that are eight shades too dark and concealers five shades too light. Is it over yet? Have they all stopped? Tell me when it's safe to open my eyes.

1990's Blush- If you are still applying your blush from your ear to your nose, girl, you are doing it all wrong. I know that's what momma taught you, but how long ago did she learn? Blush is supposed to make you look like you are flushing. That happens on the apples of your cheek, not like a hot pink racing stripe was painted across your face. I can see you from a mile away. Imagine the amount of money you will save not using that pigment all over your face! Cut it down by 2/3 and watch your money pile up.

The Rigor Mortis Lip- The funeral home just called and they want their lipstick back. We should just put you in the casket and close it up, because you look dead. Stay away from those grey, ashy-toned, mocha-brown lips. Ugh, I can't even deal. Also, lips should never be lighter than your skin tone. This completely washes the life out of your face.

Frosted Lipstick- I just can't believe companies out there are still manufacturing this. Lipsticks with silver metallic frost have BEEN out. I think since the Stone Age, to be exact.

Overdrawn Lips- Exactly who do you think you are fooling? It just looks like you can't color inside the lines. This is what lip injections are for! If you want fuller lips, go get lip filler. Even my Mom is guilty of this. She loves to line those upper lips like the arches of McDonald's (I love you, Mom). Stay inside the lines ladies. Smaller lips look way better than overdrawn lips.

No Bottom Eyeliner- Please, for the love of God, stop applying hard, unblended bottom eyeliner. This look is not flattering. I did it, we all did it, but that was forever ago. You look old and unbalanced. Now, all of you ladies have homework to do. Each one of you has to tell five friends that wear bottom eyeliner to stop, teacher's orders.

White Eyeliner- I stopped using this is 2001, and you should have as well. Whether it is on the waterline, across your eyelid, or creatively drawn under your brow, it is never okay. If you want to brighten the lower waterline to reduce redness, try using a beige or flesh-toned pencil.

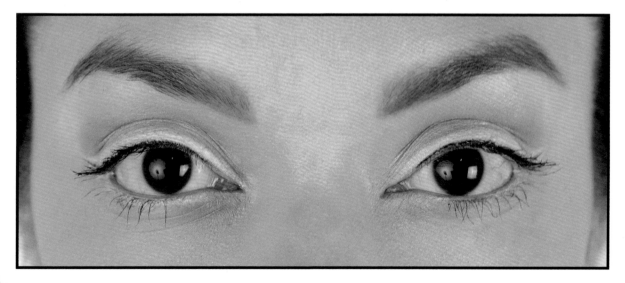

<u>Mascara on Lower Lashes</u>- Same rule of thumb as the bottom liner. When you accentuate and lengthen the lashes at the bottom of the eye, it drags you down. Makeup is supposed to lift you up! Stop wearing mascara on the bottom. Also, be careful to not over apply mascara. When you blink, right after application, the mascara that transfers to the bottom lashes is all you need.

<u>Pearlized Brow Highlighter</u>- Did someone say "Disco Ball"? I hate when I am talking to someone and see frosted eyeshadow placed under the brow, on the brow bone. FYI, I can't hear you speaking. I'm just trying to formulate a plan to wipe it all off when you aren't looking.

<u>Overly-Tweezed Brows</u>- Just go to a professional for brow shaping. Then, you can maintain the shape monthly at home. Once a year, at least, go have someone get you back on track to reshape them. Brows are so important to frame the face. Women with bad brows can't be trusted. If you over-tweezed long ago and they won't grow back, try using a brow serum to stimulate growth.

<u>Quotation or Comma Brow</u>- Do you have a bubble with a line drawn off the side? This type of brow has all sorts of names. Tadpole Brow is also a term used commonly. Brows should have a smooth transition from the inner corner, up to the arch. I'm sorry, your brows didn't grow like this. Put your tweezers down and let a professional take over.

Bleached Brows- No. Just no. Brows should match the darkest part of a blonde's hair. Please do not ever put bleach in your brows.

Dirty Makeup Brushes- Some people just don't know. My favorite is when I ask a group of women how often they are supposed to wash their makeup brushes and someone so confidently responds, "Once a year!" I wonder how often they wash their panties? Not washing your makeup brushes is gross. I don't want to be the one to have to tell this, but you have poop particles on your makeup brushes. What happens when you flush the toilet with the lid open in your bathroom that you share with your makeup vanity? What about wandering through a shoping mall, touching an escalator, and then scratching your face before going home and touching up your makeup before dinner? You are transferring all of those coodies to your brushes, and then you say you wash them once a year? Yuck! Make the first Sunday of every month "Brush Wash Day."

# Top 20 items to toss out of your makeup bag:

1. White eyeliner pencil
2. White all-over eyeshadow
3. Mocha-brown lipstick
4. Clay-toned, frosted lipstick
5. Black eyeliner pencils
6. Clumpy mascara with fibers
7. Mascara over 90 days old with lash mite infestation
8. Toners that contain alcohol
9. Waterproof, matte under eye concealer
10. All makeup brushes dropping hair
11. Old eyelash curlers with worn down pads
12. Green correctors
13. Contour kits with three ashy-toned bronzers and a super white 'baking' powder
14. Any creamy product opened and used that is over two years old
15. Any blush or bronzer over five years old
16. Matte, dry foundation
17. Eyebrow stencil kits
18. Sponge tip eyeshadow applicators
19. All sponges
20. Dry, matte, cakey foundation

Remember, if you are more visual, all of my techniques can be found on my YouTube Channel. Search: ***Jentry Kelley.*** Most videos are 3-5 minutes, and are broken down into categories. This way, you can only watch the videos on the techniques you need help with.

# Chapter 12
## "Follow Your Dreams"

___

The Sky is the Limit

Believe it or not, I was never a risk taker. I always played it safe with my job, and with my money. I even balanced my checkbook until I was 29 years old. Who still does that? I didn't overspend, always paid my bills on time, and gave myself an allowance each paycheck. I never thought that I was good enough or smart enough to be a true entrepreneur. Maybe it's because I was scared of failing. Or that I would lose everything I worked so hard for. The funny thing is, I didn't have much to lose in the grand scheme of things. Worst case scenario, I would have to move back home with my parents if I tried something and it didn't work out. So what?

Luckily, so far, my business has exceeded all my expectations, and still continues to surprise me as I watch it expand. Actually, I've always set low goals for myself and I'm not sure why. When I first started this, I kept surpassing my goals over and over before I realized I wasn't giving myself enough credit. I really could do anything I set my mind to. Why not? I didn't need a ton of money to make it work because I never really had any. If I wanted something bad enough, I would find a way to make it work.

Money is the main factor that I feel holds most people back from taking these kinds of risks to follow their dreams. We are so afraid of having to start over. Who cares if you make a mistake on your first try? With anything in life, did you always give up the first time you failed at something? What makes those who are great at anything? The person who gets up and tries over and over and over until they get it right. After they get it right, they learn how to perfect it. That's how you become successful.

Many entrepreneurs wouldn't agree with me, but I believe a small part of this was luck. Being in the right place, at the right time, with the right idea. But the majority of success comes from hard work. You know, the blood sweat and tears part. You can have all the luck in the world, but if you don't have follow through, you aren't going anywhere.

The luck part was my landing a job at the makeup counter at 18. I was going to college for a business degree, and my mom just happened to know somebody who got me the job at the makeup counter. It was only supposed to be a college job, but instead it became my career. I could've chosen to work anywhere while attending college, but I got lucky when I was hired by a makeup line with little to no professional experience in the field.

I also feel like you are either born with it, or you're not. Even as a child, I was always looking for something to sell. I would bug my parents to let me clean out the closet and the attic to find items to have a garage sale. When all the closets in our house were gutted, I would beg my mom to take me to grandma's house. She had a giant garage loaded to the brim with junk, and I wanted to sell it! I would get up at sunrise, put up the poster boards around the neighborhood advertising my sale, and every time I actually made money. It was an adrenaline rush. Not the actual cash part, but the fact that people showed up and bought what I was selling. I never really spent the money. I was frugal and saved it. I just liked when my garage sales were successful and my table of junk that I had gathered was clear. I was like this for school fundraisers selling chocolates as well. I wouldn't ask my mom to take the form to work to sell to her employees, and do all the work for me, like the other kids did. I got out there and slung those World Famous Chocolate bars myself. I knew I could get the most out of my time spent by soliciting my chocolates at the mall. I didn't know the rules, nor did I care. Nobody stopped me, and I just so happened to be the top seller for that fundraiser at school.

I always worked hard at whatever I did, and I always wanted to be the best. If you want to start a business because you want freedom and time to relax, and your 40 hour a week job is killing you, you are so far from reality. Owning a business takes a part of you that you will never get back. The freedom to relax on a beach and escape the everyday struggles will never be your life again. There is still a bit of freedom you have when working for someone else, and it's your time off the clock. When you own a company, you never have off, ever. I literally can no longer pay attention to a movie all the way through without stopping to take care of something work related. But I am okay with that, because I never really liked sitting still. That's what gives me anxiety. Trying to take one full day off of work is too much for me to handle. I always feel overwhelmingly guilty, like I can be doing more in this world and I'm wasting time when I am idling.

At the end of the day, you have to want it. You have to believe in yourself. You have to get up and try again and again, even when you don't want to. It's the people that find a way around the road blocks that become successful, not the people who give up when it seems impossible. It's about finding solutions to the problems and moving forward when you make mistakes. The people who can't control their emotions, get super stressed, and dwell on negativity never prosper. They give up and come to the conclusion that it's just not worth it. Being an entrepreneur isn't for everyone, but it's never too late to get out there and try.

I look at each experience in my life as a different chapter. Another chance to do something different, and do it even better than last time. It's never too late, and you're never too old. You just have to be able to take a risk. Find a solution where you see there is a problem, and find a way to fix it so you can show others. Make sure whatever you choose is your obsession because you have to be able to eat, sleep, and breathe that every day of your life. When times get hard, and they will, just do what I do. I close my eyes and I try to imagine me doing something else. Anything else. I literally can't even picture myself any other place than where I am now. That's how I know that I've chosen the right path, and that there's no other place for me to go. I have to make it work, and I always do. It's what gets me through the rough spots when I have uncertainty about what to do next. I'm human, and I have emotions just like you. I know it's realllllly hard to beleive, but I am imperfect. I make mistakes everyday, and feel extrememly pressured to meet everyone's expectations daily. It sounds cliché, but I know I can do anything in the world that I set your mind to, and so can you. You just have to get out there and try to learn how to apply yourself every single day without giving up. If I can do it, as lazy as I can be in my soft and fluffy bed, you can too. Just don't over think it, get up and do it. I promise you won't regret at least trying.

---